Life Cycle Costin
for Construction

Authors and Steering Committee

This report was sponsored by the Quantity Surveyors Division of the Royal Institution of Chartered Surveyors and was prepared at the Department of Construction Management, University of Reading, between April 1981 and February 1983 by:

Roger Flanagan
MSc PhD ARICS MCIOB (Quantity Surveyor)

George Norman
MA PhD (Economist)

with

J. David Furbur
ARICS (General Practice Surveyor)
Department of Surveying, Liverpool Polytechnic

The Steering Committee appointed by the RICS comprised:

Geoffrey M. Townsend JP FRICS FCIOB (Chairman)
Graham A. J. Smith ARICS Dip(CE)
Patrick Venning FRICS MACostE

The authors would like to thank Joan van Emden and Philip Yorke for their editorial guidance.

Foreword

The Quantity Surveyors Divisional Council of the Royal Institution of Chartered Surveyors is aware of the importance to the profession of a dynamic research and development programme and to this end a number of research studies are regularly commissioned through the Quantity Surveyors (Research and Development) Committee.

The process of life cycle costing is an important development and one in which chartered quantity surveyors are already taking the lead. As an area where I have had some personal involvement for a number of years, it gives me very great pleasure to write the foreword to this the first document which defines and explains the process of life cycle costing for the benefit of practitioners and clients.

The study, which has been financed by the RICS Education Trust, was carried out by Dr Roger Flanagan MSc ARICS and Dr George Norman MA, both of the University of Reading who have extensive experience in this field in the UK and internationally. They were assisted by J. David Furbur ARICS of Liverpool Polytechnic. Whilst the commissioning and steering of the work has been the responsibility of a steering group appointed by the QS (Research and Development) Committee, the views expressed and conclusions drawn are those of the authors alone.

I should like to thank in particular, on behalf of the QS Divisional Council, Roger Flanagan and George Norman for the time and effort they have expended on this study. Thanks are also due to Geoffrey Townsend who chaired the steering group and to the members of that group itself for their help and advice during the preparation of the document.

Roy Swanston
President (1982-83)
Quantity Surveyors Division

Life Cycle Costing for Construction

Contents

Chapter 1

Key Points

- The life cycle cost of an asset is the total cost of that asset over its operating life (para 1.1).

- Life cycle cost techniques are of particular relevance to the building industry (para 1.6).

- Long term costs of building can far outweigh initial capital costs and should have a much stronger influence on building design decisions than is currently the case (para 1.14).

- It is essential that quantity surveyors in the building industry be able to offer total cost advice and become proficient in life cycle cost methods (para 1.19).

- Life cycle costing will offer important benefits when applied to existing as well as to new buildings (para 1.23).

1

Life cycle cost: preliminary concepts

Introduction

1.1 The life cycle cost of an asset is defined as the total cost of that asset over its operating life, including initial acquisition costs and subsequent running costs. A life cycle cost approach, that is, an approach that takes explicit account of the life cycle cost of assets, is essential to effective decision-making in four main ways.

1.2 First, it identifies the *total* cost commitment undertaken in the acquisition of any asset, rather than merely concentrating on the initial capital costs.

1.3 Secondly, it facilitates an effective choice between alternative methods of achieving a stated objective, e.g. choosing between two different machines to perform a particular production process, or two different designs for a commercial building. It takes full account of the probability that the various options are likely to exhibit somewhat different patterns of capital and running costs, and provides a set of techniques for expressing those costs in consistent, comparable terms.

1.4 Thirdly, a life cycle cost approach is a management tool that details the current operating costs of assets such as machinery, individual building elements (heating systems, roof coverings), or complete building systems.

1.5 Finally, life cycle costing identifies those areas in which operating costs might be reduced, either by a change in operating practice, e.g. hours of operation, or by changing the relevant system.

1.6 While life cycle cost techniques can be applied in any area of economic decision making, they are particularly relevant to the proper identification and evaluation of the costs of durable assets. As a result, they are of especial relevance to the building industry. Whether complete buildings or individual building elements are considered, a decision is being made to acquire assets that are intended to last and to be used for a number of years. These assets will commit the owner or user not only to initial capital costs, but also to subsequent running costs, day to day operating, cleaning and maintenance costs, and periodic repair or replacement costs. Equally importantly, decisions made at the initial design stage will invariably affect future running costs and the economic use of the building. For instance there are numerous ways to heat a building, to illuminate it, to clad it, and divide the space into workable areas, each with different initial and running cost profiles.

1.7 Owners and users should, therefore, be encouraged to look upon their buildings in the same way as any other productive units such as plant, machinery or equipment. The cost of ownership should be planned and managed throughout the life cycle of the building, but especially at the early design stage.

1.8 Experience has indicated that decisions should be made on the basis of the total life cycle cost of a building and not just the initial capital cost. The basic premise of life cycle cost is that, to an investor, *all* costs (future as well as present) arising from an investment decision are potentially important. Thus total life cycle cost should be seen as essential in the decision-making process from the beginning, and must be considered as a major evaluation criterion in the design brief.

1.9 One major complication arises in the adoption of such a total life cycle cost approach. The relevant costs are a combination of capital costs (incurred at the initial acquisition stage) and running costs (incurred at varying points during the subsequent operation of the building or building component). Since these costs are incurred at different times they cannot be treated identically, "money today" not being equivalent to "money tomorrow". A life cycle cost approach must have as a central feature the presentation of current and future costs in equivalent terms.

2

Life cycle cost in the building industry

1.10 It is probably true to say that decisions in the building industry with respect either to the design of complete buildings, or the choice of individual building elements, have traditionally been based on a comparison of initial capital costs. This decision method has the undoubted merit of (relative) simplicity, and has been justified on two main grounds.

● It has been argued that initial capital cost is the single, most important cost commitment undertaken when purchasing either complete buildings or individual building systems. All other costs are "unimportant" and can be ignored.

● It has been suggested that, since capital cost is the single most important cost, the lowest capital cost option will also be the lowest total cost option. The implication is that there are no real benefits to be gained from reducing running costs by increasing capital costs.

1.11 Both arguments are now being challenged. Even if capital costs were dominant in the past (and this is open to question) it is being forcefully argued that this is no longer the case. Two recent "horror stories" illustrate this point.

1.12 First, a recent lead story from a provincial newspaper stated that the "Borough Council's running cost on new office building reaches £1.3 million for 1980-81". The Council in question had spent 5 years in deciding whether to build a new £5.7 million headquarters. The building was completed and occupied in 1977. It is only now that the question is being posed as to how much of the £1.3 million could have been reduced or avoided by a total cost approach in the design stage.

1.13 Secondly, a major industrial client stated that if the running costs of his United Kingdom Head Office – completed some six years ago – had been calculated then a completely different building would have been commissioned.

1.14 The basic point of both stories is that, while initial costs are clear and visible at an early stage, longer term costs are not. Nevertheless, these longer term costs can far outweigh initial capital costs, and should have a much stronger influence on decisions with respect to buildings and building elements than is currently the case.

1.15 This is illustrated in *figures 1.1* and *1.2. Figure 1.1* illustrates the life cycle cost commitment for a small primary school built for a United Kingdom Local Authority. In this *figure*, running costs, which are incurred either annually or at periodic intervals over the life of the school, are compared with capital costs, which are incurred at the initial construction stage. As was noted above, for such a comparison to be valid, future costs have to be converted (discounted) to their current equivalent. The techniques for making this conversion, discounted cash flow, are presented in chapter 4. Suffice it to say at this stage that a 2% discount rate (net of inflation) was applied by the Local Authority to all future costs and the life of the school – the life cycle of the analysis – has been assumed to be 50 years.

1.16 As can be seen, capital costs account for well under half of the total cost commitment, being only 2.3% greater than combined cleaning and caretaking, replacement and maintenance, and routine servicing costs.

1.17 *Figure 1.2* illustrates the life cycle cost commitment for a new flooring system installed in an engineering facility. In this case a 10% discount rate has been used, but maintenance and replacement costs are assumed to escalate at 4%. A life cycle of 25 years is assumed.

1.18 Again, it can be seen that concentration solely on initial capital cost will give a very imperfect view of the actual costs being incurred.

1.19 This discussion can be summarised by stating that the client of *figure 1.3*, concerned with, or informed of, short term considerations only is a thing of the past. It is becoming increasingly important for quantity surveyors in the building industry to offer total cost advice and become proficient in life cycle cost methods on which such advice is based.

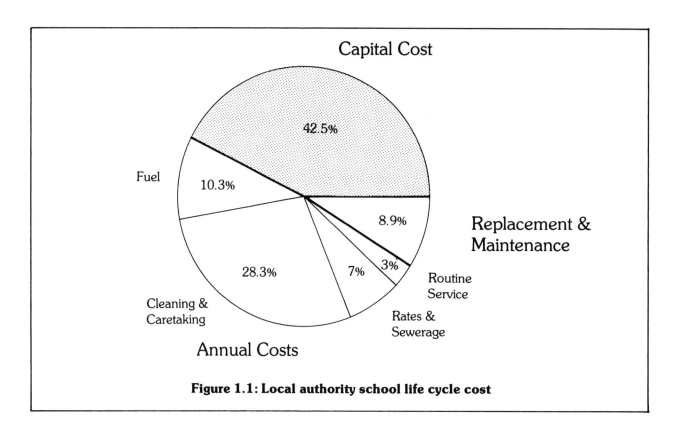

Figure 1.1: Local authority school life cycle cost

1.20   It should be stated that life cycle cost techniques have not been completely ignored in building design. Some designers do make life cycle cost allowances in particular types of construction and with respect to particular building elements. Nevertheless, it is fair to argue that the use of the techniques remains unsatisfactory. One reason for this is probably lack of familiarity with life cycle costing. In addition, there are important institutional constraints that must be overcome. Many public sector clients, for example, are required to use capital cost as the sole criterion in decision-making. Indeed, most public sector funding arrangements separate capital and revenue budgets, thus imposing severe restrictions on a total cost approach.

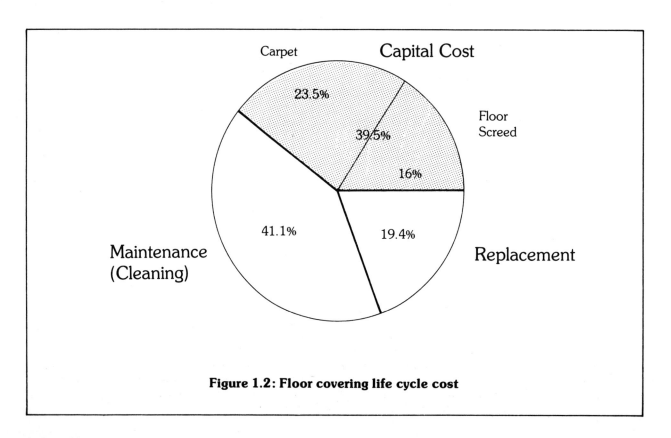

Figure 1.2: Floor covering life cycle cost

1.21 The second argument noted above, that the lowest capital cost option will also be the lowest total cost option, is also open to question. It is based in part on the relative dominance of capital costs, and the discussion above indicates how weak that argument is. In addition, any number of recent examples can be produced to challenge the "minimum capital cost" approach to decision-making. It is no longer the case, for example, that double glazing or building insulation are considered as expensive luxuries.

1.22 In other areas also, it can be shown that a total cost approach can generate significant cost savings. A recent example is outlined in *figure 1.4*. Two floor covering options were presented to a client – a wood block floor or carpet over a screeded floor. As can be seen, the carpet covering is preferred in a total cost approach despite the fact that this option has the higher initial cost. It offers significant savings on annual maintenance costs – particularly on cleaning costs – that are sufficient to offset the additional initial and subsequent replacement costs.

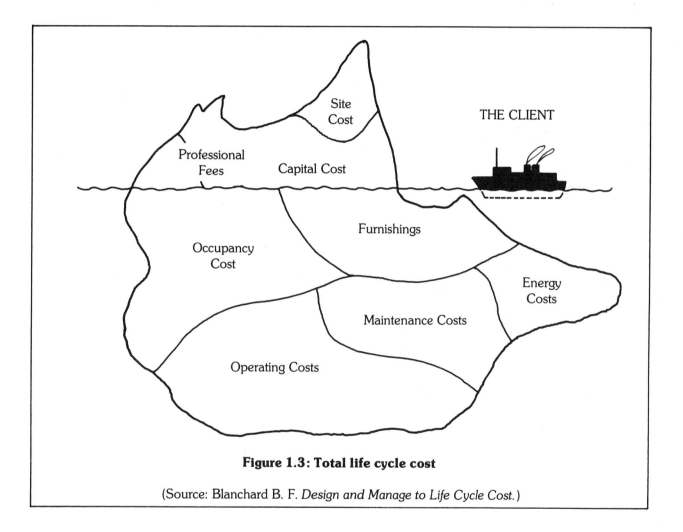

Figure 1.3: Total life cycle cost

(Source: Blanchard B. F. *Design and Manage to Life Cycle Cost.*)

1.23 It might be thought from this discussion that the main area of application for life cycle cost is with respect to new buildings or the individual elements of new buildings. This is not the case. A life cycle cost approach also offers potential cost savings when applied to the existing building stock. Indeed, this is probably one of the most important areas of application of life cycle cost techniques in the building industry.

1.24 Buildings are durable assets, and while new buildings are continually being added to the existing stock, the majority of building users will be making decisions with regard to existing buildings. At the same time, the durability of buildings implies that design decisions made during their initial construction, while perhaps correct at the time, may well need to be altered to adjust for unforeseen changes in economic conditions. In an era of low energy costs it would have been difficult to justify double or triple glazing solely on cost grounds, whereas it might now be sensible to change existing glazing systems. The move towards

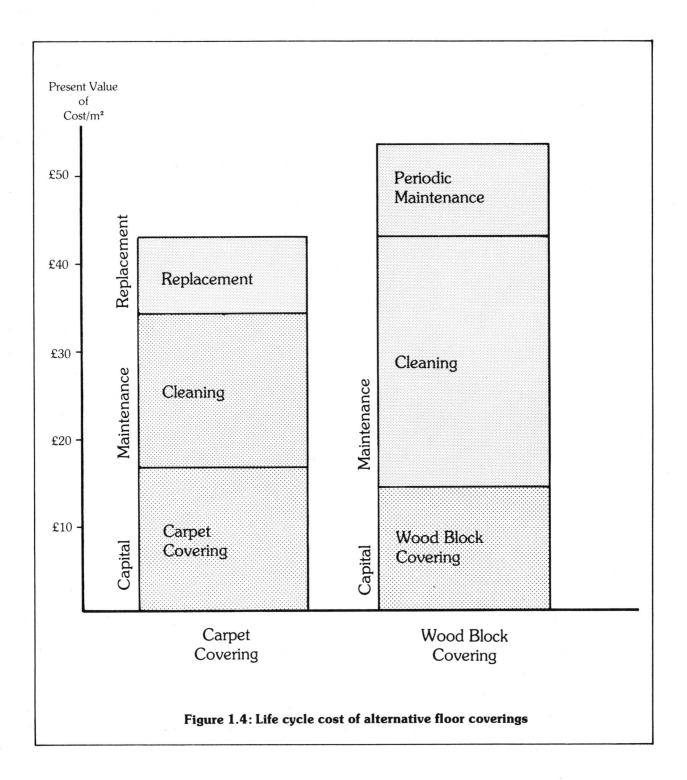

Figure 1.4: Life cycle cost of alternative floor coverings

materials that are easy to clean and maintain is driven at least in part by the increase in labour costs relative to other costs. A life cycle cost approach will identify the potential for such design changes.

1.25 It should be noted that for a life cycle cost approach to be effective in reducing the running costs of existing buildings it is necessary that these running costs be monitored. In other words, life cycle cost should be seen also as an essential element of overall cost management. It can identify in detail one major area in which an organization incurs costs – the operation of buildings – and point to ways in which potential cost savings might be achieved.

Conclusions and objectives

1.26 While the "minimum capital cost" approach might not have been totally wrong in the past in the choice of buildings or building elements, this can no longer be assumed to be the case. It is of increasing importance that a life cycle cost approach be adopted at the early design stage and in the management of the existing building stock.

1.27 Life cycle cost will loosen the decision-maker's traditional concentration on capital costs to the almost total exclusion of any concern with future running costs. There must be a recognition that decisions made today carry cost implications in the future, whether these decisions relate to the design of a complete building, or to the choice of an individual component. Further, once an organization begins to apply life cycle cost techniques it will gain a further advantage through a continuous learning and monitoring process. An historical data base will be built up that will make it easier to identify future areas of potential cost reduction.

1.28 This is not to say that the implementation of life cycle cost in the building industry will be straightforward. Indeed, it is precisely because the industry exhibits particular characteristics and poses particular problems in the use of life cycle cost techniques that this book is necessary. The nature of the construction process and the length of time separating the design and the operation/user phases make the transmission of user performance data more difficult than in other industries. In addition buildings are complex, and individual building elements interact in a diversity of ways, for example, a change in plan shape or building aspect will affect not only the initial construction costs, but also subsequent heating, lighting and other operating costs.

1.29 Nevertheless, it is essential that design teams in the United Kingdom develop the expertise necessary to offer life cycle cost advice to their clients. Undoubted benefits will accrue to clients from such advice. Further, the design teams will be better able to meet the challenge of design teams from other countries who are now applying life cycle cost techniques in their domestic markets and so offering such a service as part of the "package" on international contracts. In the United States of America, for example, many States now require a life cycle cost plan to be prepared at the design stage on public building contracts.

1.30 The major objective of this book is to try to cut through the complicating factors noted above and to present in a straightforward and comprehensible way the principles, techniques and use of life cycle costing. The intention is:

- To identify the benefits of a life cycle approach to owners and users of buildings.

- To explain and illustrate the techniques used in life cycle costing.

- To present a standardised set of procedures whereby the life cycle cost approach can be implemented in the building industry.

1.31 Subsequent chapters will take up and treat in more detail the preliminary concepts introduced above. Chapter 2 presents an overview of the basic life cycle cost techniques, and discusses the relevance of these techniques to different types of client. In chapter 3 the main components of a life cycle cost approach to building are developed, while in chapter 4 the central technical procedures (i.e. discounted cash flow) are explained. Chapter 5 suggests alternative sources of data for life cycle cost studies and chapter 6 discusses methods for recording and presenting the information. The techniques are then illustrated in chapters 7 and 8 by applying them to maintenance costs, rates and energy costs, and to the tax planning of buildings. Chapter 9 presents a worked example and the main conclusions are then summarised in chapter 10.

Chapter 2

Key Points

- The onus lies with the client's professional advisers to ensure that clients are made fully aware of the potential benefits of a life cycle cost approach (para. 2.2).

- It is reasonable to expect that real incomes and energy costs will continue to rise, further increasing the importance of running costs relative to capital costs (para. 2.3).

- If life cycle cost is to be effective it must be implemented as early as possible in the design process (para. 2.9).

- The reason for using life cycle cost will vary with the type of client, and with the experience of clients (paras. 2.13 to 2.17).

- Life cycle cost represents a particular application of classical investment appraisal techniques (para. 2.25).

- The life cycle is the time horizon over which the study is being conducted (para. 2.36).

- The period of time over which money has been borrowed to finance the building is not a suitable choice of life cycle (para. 2.44).

- No hard and fast guidelines can be given as to the "correct" choice of life cycle (para. 2.44).

- A distinction must be drawn between the expected life of a building and the expected lives of the various building components (para. 2.45).

2

A brief overview of life cycle cost

The importance of life cycle cost

2.1 It may seem rather obvious to suggest that the decision-maker should examine the total cost implications of any decision. All consumers apply this concept in a more or less formal fashion when considering expenditure on consumer durables such as cars, freezers or houses. The consequences of not doing so are clear. Nevertheless, as was argued in chapter 1, it is probably true to state that within the UK life cycle cost has not been generally implemented within the building industry. Several reasons for this apparent failing can be suggested.

2.2 Firstly, ignorance on the part of the client cannot be discounted, as is illustrated in *figure 1.3*. The majority of clients are not "in the business" of building; they require a building, whether it be a factory, office or commercial premises, as an input to their main productive activity. As a result, they may well be totally unaware that design options that increase their initial outlay may significantly reduce their future operating costs. In such cases the onus lies increasingly with the clients' professional advisers to ensure that clients are made fully aware of the options open to them.

2.3 Secondly, it must be recognised that the main impetus to life cycle cost in building emanates from the increase in relative importance of labour, materials and energy costs over the last decade. It would appear that clients and professionals within the building industry have been slow to recognise that these changes in the economic climate have upset the balance between capital and running costs of buildings. As long as running costs were relatively low, there was little, if anything, to be lost by using minimum capital cost as a selection criterion. But the changes in relative costs now being experienced are sufficiently great as to demand a change in perspective within the industry. It is reasonable to expect that real incomes and energy costs will continue to rise, further increasing the importance of running costs relative to capital costs.

2.4 Thirdly, the classic form of life cycle cost cuts across the traditional separation of capital and operating budget functions. The starting point of a life cycle cost approach is that capital and operating costs are intimately linked and should not be treated separately. It follows that if management decisions and control systems are to be compatible with life cycle cost output and recommendations, there must be at least some, if not complete, integration of capital and operating budget procedures. The problem was mentioned in chapter 1 (paragraph 1.20) as it applies to public authorities in the United Kingdom. There is no doubt, however, that it also applies within many private sector organizations.

2.5 In addition to these general factors, there are also problems specific to the building industry which have inhibited the implementation of a life cycle cost approach. In particular, it is necessary to design standard methods for collecting relevant data, to determine just what are "relevant data", and to develop standard techniques and documentation by which these data can be analysed.

2.6 Even where data are available, additional efforts are required by the principal decision makers in the design team to analyse the user performance costs. The problem is not so much a lack of ideas; ideas are historically what design teams are best at providing. The task confronting them is dealing with limited economic resources in such a way that optimum proposals are selected and implemented.

2.7 Finally, the output of the building industry is complex, often very sophisticated, and generally non-standardised. Decisions with respect to one element of a building carry implications, both directly and indirectly, for many other elements. These interactions and interrelationships are often difficult to untangle but dangerous to ignore, as indicated by the schematic diagram in *figure 2.1*. Thus, there are not only connections between initial capital costs and subsequent running costs, but also between the many elements that make up recurrent operations and maintenance costs. For example, more frequent cleaning of light sources will increase luminosity and so reduce lighting costs. At the same time, different decisions with respect to lighting will affect future cleaning costs, and maintenance costs.

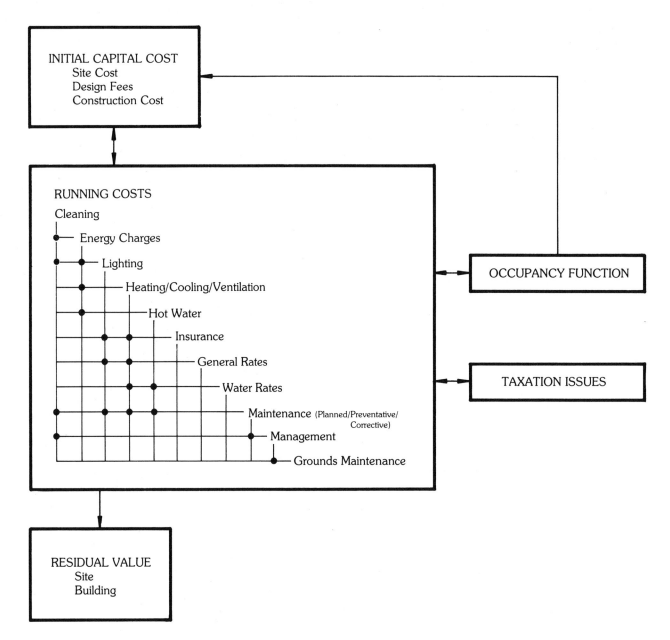

Figure 2.1: Interdependencies between major cost areas

2.8 No matter what the reasons for the past neglect of life cycle cost, there is no longer any doubt that the building industry must take account of the long term implications of current design decisions. The relative balance between fixed, (initial capital costs), and variable (operations and maintenance costs) has changed and there is no reason to believe that labour, materials and energy costs will fall in relative terms in the future. In other words, if all efficient design options were to be ranked in ascending order of their capital costs, and so in descending order of their recurrent operating and maintenance costs (all expressed in current values), *figure 2.2 (a)* might have been characteristic of cost conditions in the past: the minimum capital cost design option also being the minimum total (life cycle) cost option. But the more likely case in future is that illustrated in *figure 2.2 (b)*. It will often, perhaps typically, be preferable to incur higher initial capital costs in order to secure lower future running costs, and this whether complete buildings or individual building elements are being considered.

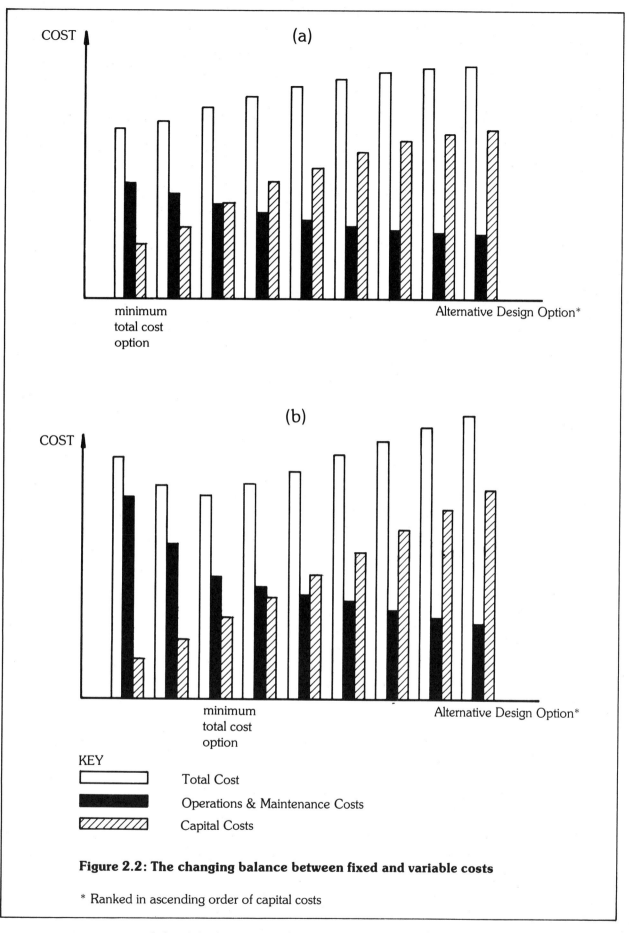

Figure 2.2: The changing balance between fixed and variable costs

* Ranked in ascending order of capital costs

2.9 A further point must be emphasised. If life cycle cost is to be effective it must be implemented as early as possible in the design process. As can be seen from *figure 2.3*, the later life cycle cost techniques are introduced during the design process the lower will be the potential for cost savings and the more expensive it will be to implement any design changes suggested by the results of the analysis.

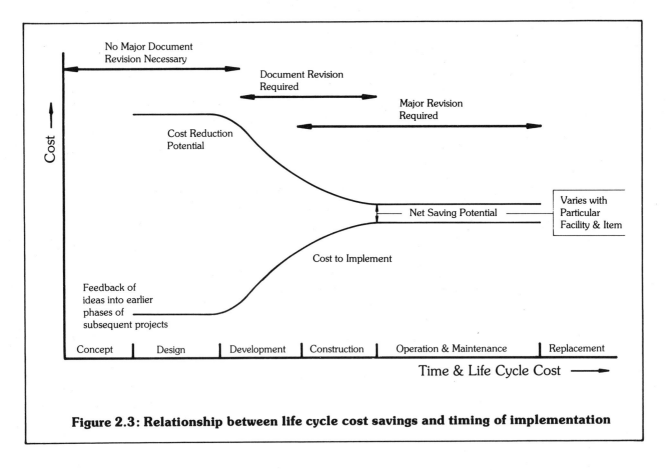

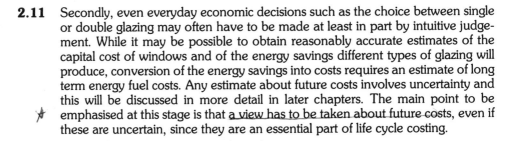

Figure 2.3: Relationship between life cycle cost savings and timing of implementation

2.10 Two words of caution are relevant at this point. First, it might be felt that life cycle cost techniques will automatically reject the least capital cost option. This is wrong. There will undoubtedly continue to be many cases in which such an option is also the least total cost option. Life cycle costing ensures that such an option is chosen for the correct reasons and after proper comparison.

2.11 Secondly, even everyday economic decisions such as the choice between single or double glazing may often have to be made at least in part by intuitive judgement. While it may be possible to obtain reasonably accurate estimates of the capital cost of windows and of the energy savings different types of glazing will produce, conversion of the energy savings into costs requires an estimate of long term energy fuel costs. Any estimate about future costs involves uncertainty and this will be discussed in more detail in later chapters. The main point to be emphasised at this stage is that a view has to be taken about future costs, even if these are uncertain, since they are an essential part of life cycle costing.

2.12 Life cycle costing is not the universal panacea for the building industry, but when properly understood and used it is a useful and powerful tool.

Different client motivations for the use of life cycle cost

2.13 Clients of the construction industry cover a wide range of interests and have different requirements and motivations. The reasons for using life cycle cost will vary with the type of client. For example, a public sector client usually builds to satisfy a public need whereas the private sector client will be much more influenced by the impact of the project on his profitability.

2.14 In general terms clients can be classified as follows.

● Private sector owner-occupiers who commission buildings for their own occupation.

● Public sector owner-occupiers who commission buildings for their own occupation. This group will include central and local government and nationalised industries.

● Public sector clients who build for sale, lease and rental, such as development corporations, and local authority housing departments.

- Developers whose prime function is to develop and finance buildings for sale or for rent, either speculatively or for a known client. There has been a growing tendency for developers to provide a sophisticated service in assembling the ingredients for a development, undertaking it, and subsequently managing it in return for a share of occupational rents from the institution funding the development, or alternatively for a fee based on performance.

- Financial institutions which include pension funds, insurance companies, property unit trusts, charities and banks, which provide finance for the development projects. Some financial institutions have become directly involved in development. However, institutions will take strictly limited risks with no planning or Development Land Tax problems, preferably freehold or with a lease of 125 years or more. The institutions will also often purchase completed buildings as investments.

- Lessee-occupier who rents space in a building on the basis of a landlord and tenant relationship. This system allows each party to own a separate legal interest which can be managed or marketed unilaterally.

2.15 The different experience of particular types of client will also affect their perception of life cycle cost, and implies a further classification of clients into those who:

- Build only once in their lives.

- Have a limited development programme and build once every two or three years.

- Have a large continuing development programme.

2.16 The life cycle cost process must take into account not only the client type, but also the investor motivation because some clients may choose to invest irrespective of the total cost consequences. Industrialists invest in buildings primarily to meet additional demand or as a consequnce of technological change. The purchase of new machinery may dictate the need for additional floorspace or alterations to existing buildings to allow for more height, air conditioning, and so on. In the NEDO report "Construction for Industrial Recovery" (1978), 109 firms out of 299 gave this as one of their reasons for investment. The owner-occupier has similar needs. For example, the department store owner might invest to increase the sales area or to create a new image for the company. The question of the client image may be important as many clients are prepared to pay for prestige value.

2.17 Public sector clients usually build to satisfy a public need, for example, for housing, sports complexes, schools or fire stations. Developers and financial institutions, on the other hand, invest in buildings primarily for the capital appreciation potential and the income cash flow. In addition, certain types of industrial buildings offer tax advantages to the owner: this is discussed in chapter 8.

2.18 Given this diversity of interests, the incentive for each type of client to apply life cycle cost techniques is understandably different.

2.19 The incentive for the owner-occupier, whether public or private sector, to use life cycle cost is obvious. This type of client should treat a building and individual building elements precisely as he would treat any other factor of production in his main activity.

2.20 The lessee-occupier may appear to have little obvious incentive to apply life cycle cost to a complete building, but he should apply life cycle cost to individual decisions in his use of the building systems, e.g. choice of floor finishings or installation of energy control systems. In addition, if the lessee-occupier is educated to think in life cycle cost terms he will be more attracted to efficient buildings and building systems. Such buildings will offer savings on annual service charges and general running costs, savings that will subsequently be reflected in the rents these buildings command.

2.21 When developers or financial institutions commission buildings for their own use, the incentive to use life cycle cost is that which applies to any owner-occupier. The relevance of life cycle cost to such clients when they are develop-

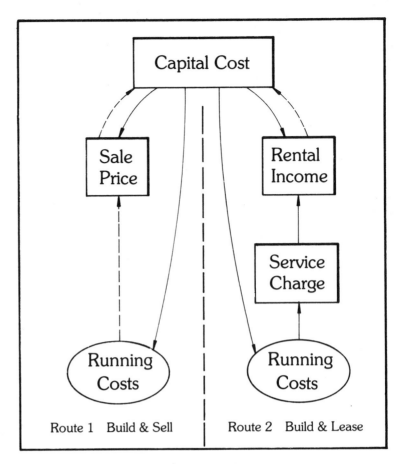

Figure 2.4: The developer's decision

ing to lease or sell is less obvious but nonetheless strong. The developer, for example, can take either of the routes illustrated in *figure 2.4*.

2.22 If the developer is commissioning a building for sale to an owner-occupier, the latter will be interested in the life cycle costs of the building. This will feed back, therefore, into the purchase price he is willing to offer. In other words, the developer should be able by appropriate marketing to reap the advantages of commissioning an efficient building.

2.23 A similar argument applies, as has already been suggested, to the case in which the developer rents the building to final users. The lease will usually contain provision for rental and service charges: some of the running costs will be passed on to the user, but the remainder will be met by the level of expenditure covered by the service charge. Improvements in running costs even at the expense of higher capital costs, will make the building more attractive to users. In a reasonably competitive market it follows that rental income will increase as a consequence of reduced running costs. Further, if the additional expenditures are justified by use of life cycle cost techniques, the increased rental will be sufficient to cover the cost of efficiency improvements. It is worth noting that the trend in the USA is towards the user paying a rental price that includes the rent and all the running costs of the building; no separate service charge is levied on the tenant. Minimizing the running costs on the building then becomes a very positive objective.

2.24 Similar arguments apply to the financial institution. The price it is willing to pay to acquire a building, by commissioning it or by purchasing from a developer, will be determined by likely rental income and possible capital appreciation. These in turn will be affected by the running costs to be met by the final user.

The implementation of life cycle cost

2.25 The major technical characteristics of the analytical tools on which life cycle cost is based have long been recognized. Life cycle cost represents a particular application of a classical financial technique, long taught and successfully employed in investment analysis, through which the time-phased costs and revenues attributable to a project over a specified planning period can be evaluated and compared with other methods for achieving a stated objective. As such, the life cycle cost concept is neither new nor complicated, and consists of the following major elements.

● Identification of an overall time period or life cycle applicable to all possibilities being evaluated (within this overall life cycle differing life cycles may exist for the various components of the alternative facility or system).

● Inclusion of all costs and revenues attributable to the project, by time period – including initial investment, recurring costs and revenues and proceeds from ultimate sale or other disposal.

● Consideration of only those costs and revenues directly attributable to the project decision under consideration.

● The effects of time, including allowance for:

  – The impact of inflation on costs incurred or revenues generated in future years.

  – The fact that pounds spent or received in the future are worth less than pounds spent or received today because of reduced interest expense or lost interest income from those pounds.

The four elements can be broken into seven basic steps necessary in implementing a life cycle cost approach.

Step 1: Establish the objective

2.26 The single most important step in the analysis is the definition of what the proposed project is intended to achieve. Typical objectives might be:

● To provide 1,000 sq m of general administrative space.

● To choose between a number of alternative glazing options.

● To commission an advance factory in a New Town.

2.27 It is essential that the wording of the objective is unbiased, in that it imposes no prior judgements on the best method for achieving the objective. Thus "build a 4 storey general administrative block" is not an unbiased statement of the first objective above.

Step 2: Choice of method

2.28 After formulating an unbiased statement of the objective, the next step is to determine the range of feasible methods for achieving that objective. Since the ultimate purpose of the life cycle cost process is to assist the decision-maker in making resource allocation decisions, it is essential that all realistic possibilities be considered. Occasionally, pre-conceived ideas or administrative constraints (such as an upper limit on initial funding) will tend to exclude certain choices. Nevertheless, all practical possibilities must be analysed.

2.29 Consider, for example, the situation in which two alternatives have been presented:

Option 1: Owner-occupation – Building A.

Option 2: Commercial lease – Building B.

Option 1 is favoured as being the lower life cycle cost option. However, a third option – owner-occupation, Building C – has not been considered because its construction cost estimate is felt to be outside capital budget constraints. Further investigation indicates that Building C offers substantial savings in running costs – so much so, in fact, that it is really the lowest life cycle cost option. The decision-taker must be advised of this option. He may still opt for Option 1, but he should do so in the knowledge that it is not the most cost-effective solution.

Step 3: Formulate assumptions

2.30 Life cycle cost deals with future expenditure and thus involves elements of uncertainty. A complete factual picture may be impossible to construct and certain assumptions will be necessary in order to proceed with the analysis, for example, it may be necessary to forecast escalation of energy, labour and materials costs. These assumptions must be clearly identified, and where possible accompanied by a statement of the basis for them. It must also be emphasised that estimates should never be used if factual data are available.

Step 4: Identify the costs and the life cycle

Cost Effective Items only

2.31 For each possible choice, the surveyor must determine the life cycle of the project and of individual components of that project, and all costs occurring during the entire project life cycle. This will often be far from simple to achieve and is one of the areas with which this book is chiefly concerned.

Step 5: Compare costs and rank the alternatives

2.32 This step is the most important element of a life cycle cost approach. Various techniques are available for ranking alternatives, for example, net present value, savings-investment ratios, internal rate of return, or annual equivalent value. These will be considered in detail in chapter 4.

Step 6: Sensitivity analysis

2.33 When the results of step 5 are not demonstrably in favour of one choice it is advisable to test the sensitivity of the analysis to certain dominant cost factors and assumptions in order to give a complete picture to the decision-maker. Sensitivity analysis techniques are discussed in more detail in chapter 4.

Step 7: Investigate capital cost constraints

2.34 Procedures for life cycle costing should include a step in which the initial costs of all recommendations are aggregated to ensure that they do not exceed the total funding available. If this constraint is exceeded, trade-off evaluations should be made until the optimum combination of lowest life cycle cost within available funding has been reached. As part of this process, the client should be sufficiently flexible to allow the quantity surveyor to adjust capital budgets where significant life cycle cost savings are indicated (recall step 2).

The output of life cycle cost

2.35 The discussion in this chapter and in chapter 1 has been somewhat abstract. Thus, while practical applications of life cycle cost will be presented in subsequent chapters, there is some benefit to be gained from a brief illustration of the form that a final life cycle cost plan can be expected to take. Such an example is detailed in table 2A.

The life cycle

2.36 An essential element of life cycle costing is the definition of the life cycle itself. The life cycle for a particular cost study is the time horizon over which the study is being conducted. Typically this will be the period for which a particular building is expected to be operated by the organization for whom the study is being conducted. As a practical and usable definition, however, this is not particularly helpful, since the problem remains of forecasting the probable operational life of a particular facility.

2.37 The life of a building is a complex expression involving many considerations. Theoretically, the lives of various elements of the building should be predicted from observed data on failure, but this type of information is rarely available. In addition, building life can be extended by periodic maintenance and replacement or may be foreshortened by changing economic, social or legal conditions. These considerations are summarized in *figure 2.5* which shows the sequence of a building life cycle for an owner-occupier.

Table 2A: Life cycle cost plan summary calculations

Project: Floor covering			Option 1: Carpet covering		Option 2: Wood block covering		Option 3:		Option 4:	
Location: New Town										
Date: 1982			Life cycle: 25 years		Life cycle: 25 years		Life cycle:		Life cycle:	
Discount rate: 10%										
Costs			Estimated costs	Present value	Estimated costs	Present value	Estimated costs	Present value	Estimated costs	Present value
I: **Capital costs**										
Floor screed (£8.99/m²)				9858		9858				
Carpet (£13.21/m²)				14484						
Wood block flooring (£9.59/m²)						10509				
Sub total				24342		20367				
Contingencies @ 5%				1217		1018				
Total capital costs				25559		21385				
II: **Running costs** II.1: **Operations costs**	Inflation rate	Inflation adjusted discount factor								
N/A										
Total operations costs				–		–				
II.2: **Maintenance costs annual**										
Carpet cleaning (£1.86/m²/year)	4%	13.085	2038	26667						
Wood block cleaning (£3.05/m²/year)	4%	13.085			3340	43704				
Woodblock refinishing (£1.11/m²/year)	4%	13.085			1222	15990				
Total maintenance costs (annual)				26667		59694				
II.3: **Maintenance/ replacement/ alterations (intermittent)**	Year	PV factor								
Carpet	10	0.5711	14484	8272						
Carpet	20	0.3268	14484	4733						
Total maintenance/replacement/ alterations costs				13005		–				
II.4: **Sundries** N/A										
Total sundries				–		–				
Total running costs				39672		59694				
III: **Additional tax allowances** Public sector client										
Total additional tax allowances				–		–				
IV: **Salvage and residuals** N/A										
Total salvage and residuals				–		–				
Total net present value of life cycle costs				65231		81079				
Annual equivalent value of life cycle costs				7187		8933				

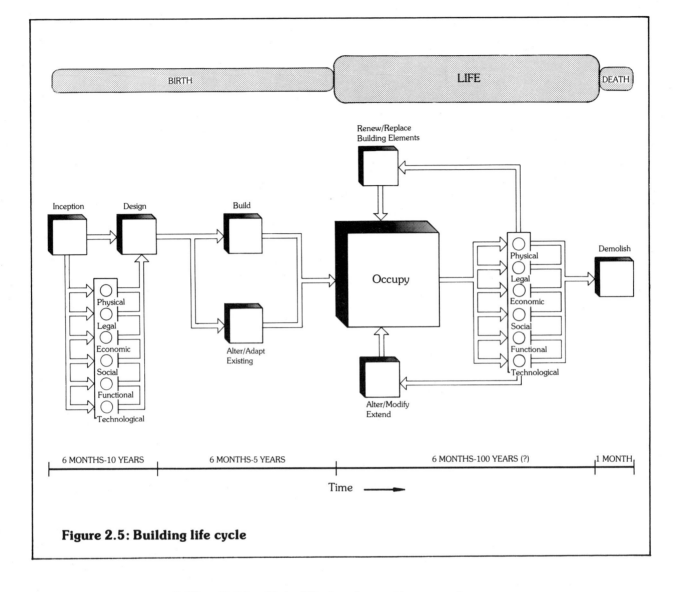

Figure 2.5: Building life cycle

2.38 Building life is difficult to forecast because of:

- Physical obsolescence
- Economic obsolescence
- Functional obsolescence
- Technological obsolescence
- Social obsolescence
- Legal obsolescence

2.39 The physical life of the building is the period from construction to the time when physical collapse is possible; in reality most buildings never reach this point as they are demolished owing to economic obsolescence.

2.40 The economic life is the period from construction to economic obsolescence, that is, the period of time over which occupation of a particular building is considered to be the least cost alternative for meeting a particular objective. This might occur when the land value of the building is worth more for potential development than the rental income derived from letting the building, or when, for a lessee-occupier, another building becomes more economically desirable.

2.41 The functional life is the period from construction to the time when the building ceases to function for the same purpose as that for which it was built. Many clients of the building industry, particularly in manufacturing industries, require a building for a process that often has a short life span. Functional and economic obsolescence are therefore closely interlinked. Functional obsolescence does not normally lead to demolition as the building will often be refurbished to fulfil another function.

2.42 Technological obsolescence occurs when the building or component is no longer technologically superior to alternatives and replacement is undertaken because of lower operating costs or greater efficiency.

2.43 Social and legal obsolescence occur when human desires dictate replacement for non-economic reasons. For example, where some aspects of safety are concerned, replacement becomes essential. Alternatively, where reliability is of the utmost concern, as in hospital buildings, replacement is undertaken.

2.44 No hard and fast guidelines can be given as to the "correct" choice of life cycle. There is, however, a strong case in favour of choosing economic or functional life. Several points must then be emphasised.

● The appropriate economic life will vary with the type of client. An owner-occupier, for example, might be expected to operate a building in a particular use for rather longer than a rent payer-lessee. When considering the investment for the public sector client a relatively long time horizon, usually commensurate with the physical life, should be used. However, some government departments are given guidelines on specific time horizons to use for investment analysis. Some clients, such as property companies, are looking for a short term financial gain. In these circumstances the time horizon will equal the clients' economic life span for the building, which is the holding period that is expected to maximise speculative profits.

● It is probably better to err on the conservative side when forecasting economic life. In addition, the discounting process, by which future costs are converted to their current equivalent, is such that the cost implications of a choice between a 25 year or 30 year life cycle will not, in general, be particularly severe.

● The period of time over which money has been borrowed to finance the building is not a suitable basis for forecasting the building life. Futhermore, any life calculated purely for taxation and depreciation purposes should not be used for life cycle cost calculations.

2.45 It must be emphasised, as implied by *figure 2.5*, that a distinction must be drawn between the expected life of a building and the expected lives of the various building components. Life cycle cost techniques should, indeed must, be applied in the choice of both complete buildings and individual building components. When looking at a building component, however, the life cycle is not, in general, the period between acquisition of the component and its eventual replacement. Rather, the component must be seen as an input to the building within which it is contained. The life cycle for the building component is then the life cycle of the building. The life cycle for the carpet covering previously used as an example is not the period within which the carpet will need to be replaced – 10 years – but rather the period of operation of the building for which the floor covering is needed. The carpet will be replaced several times during the life of the building and this must be allowed for.

Some unresolved problems

2.46 In performing the steps detailed in paragraphs 2.26 to 2.34, a number of further issues will need to be resolved besides those underlying the choice of life cycle. Firstly, it will be necessary to identify and collect the data necessary for effective analysis. This may, however, be far from straightforward. The building industry is not yet geared to the identification of running costs, or of the interrelationships between running costs and capital costs. Secondly, since the analysis takes explicit account of costs over time, there will be estimation problems, made more severe by the lack of an effective historical data base.

2.47 Inflation poses a similar problem. If all costs can be assumed to escalate at the same rate no great difficulty will arise. If, however, different cost elements typically escalate at different rates, a more complex set of techniques will be necessary.

2.48   Subsequent chapters will address themselves specifically to these issues. In some cases the techniques presented will be quite straight-forward but in other cases definitive choice criteria cannot be developed. It is then incumbent upon the quantity surveyor to provide the decision-maker with sufficient information, for example, by performing a sensitivity analysis (step 6 above) to allow choice of the most desirable option.

Chapter **3**

Key Points

- The link between capital costs and running costs must be developed in such a way that the total cost implications of a design decision can be evaluated at the design stage (para. 3.1).

- The personnel most concerned with running cost aspects of a building are not likely to be involved until the building is completed and occupied (para. 3.3).

- Estimates of running costs are based upon assumptions about future events and these assumptions must be clearly stated (para. 3.6).

- A life cycle cost approach consists of four distinct components: life cycle cost planning, full year effect costs, life cycle cost analysis, life cycle cost management (para. 3.8).

- Life cycle cost planning establishes estimated target costs for the running costs of a building or building element (paras. 3.9 to 3.17).

- Full year effect costs identify the short term running costs of a proposed building (paras. 3.18 to 3.19).

- Life cycle cost analysis identifies running costs and performances of currently operational buildings and building components (para. 3.20). It is a management tool intended to identify the actual costs incurred in operating buildings (paras. 3.21 to 3.26).

- No two buildings will have identical running costs, nor will the running costs for any specific building be the same from year to year (para. 3.25).

- There is a long time lag between design, occupation, and the availability of reliable data on running costs (para. 3.26).

- Life cycle cost management is to existing buildings what life cycle cost planning is to new buildings. It is one of the most important areas for the application of life cycle cost techniques (para. 3.30).

3

The components of a life cycle cost approach and its relationship to quantity surveying practice

Introduction

3.1 The quantity surveying profession is skilled in forecasting construction prices and in manipulating and analysing historical cost data. The profession has the expertise, therefore, to apply life cycle cost techniques. What is missing, as illustrated by *figure 3.1* is the link between the capital and running costs of buildings, such that the total cost implications of a design decision can be effectively evaluated at the design stages of a project.

3.2 It is necessary that the artificial separation between the design process and the occupancy phase be removed. *Figure 3.2* shows the various interests of the parties involved in designing and occupying a building. At the early design stages the design team is concerned with ensuring that the proposed design will meet the client's brief, in terms of function, quality and cost. As the design detail develops, the architect, structural and services engineer, and the quantity surveyor must work closely to ensure that the proposed building is economically sound in that it achieves a proper balance between capital costs and running costs.

3.3 The design team will probably seek expert advice about the expected running costs of the project. However, the personnel most concerned with the running cost aspects are not likely to be involved with the project until the building is

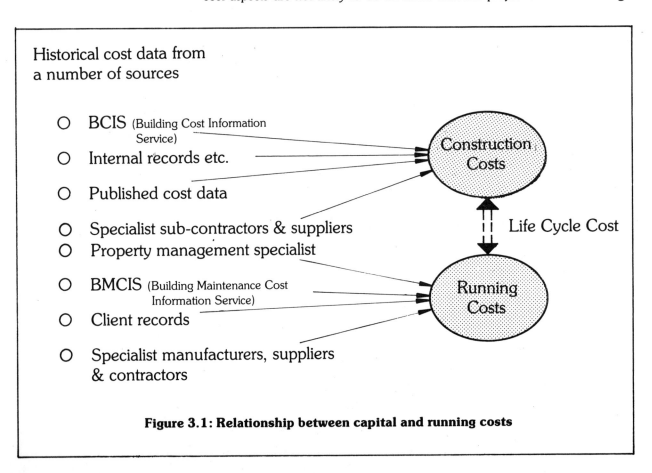

Historical cost data from
a number of sources

- ○ BCIS (Building Cost Information Service)
- ○ Internal records etc.
- ○ Published cost data
- ○ Specialist sub-contractors & suppliers
- ○ Property management specialist
- ○ BMCIS (Building Maintenance Cost Information Service)
- ○ Client records
- ○ Specialist manufacturers, suppliers & contractors

Construction Costs

Life Cycle Cost

Running Costs

Figure 3.1: Relationship between capital and running costs

completed and occupied. Furthermore, they will be drawn from a variety of disciplines. In other words, current practice is such that the design process is divorced from construction, and the building operators are divorced from the design process. This is also complicated by the long time lag between the design stage and the availability of useful data on running costs.

3.4 Parties who are likely to have an active involvement in the building when it is operational can be classified as operations staff who are involved in cleaning,

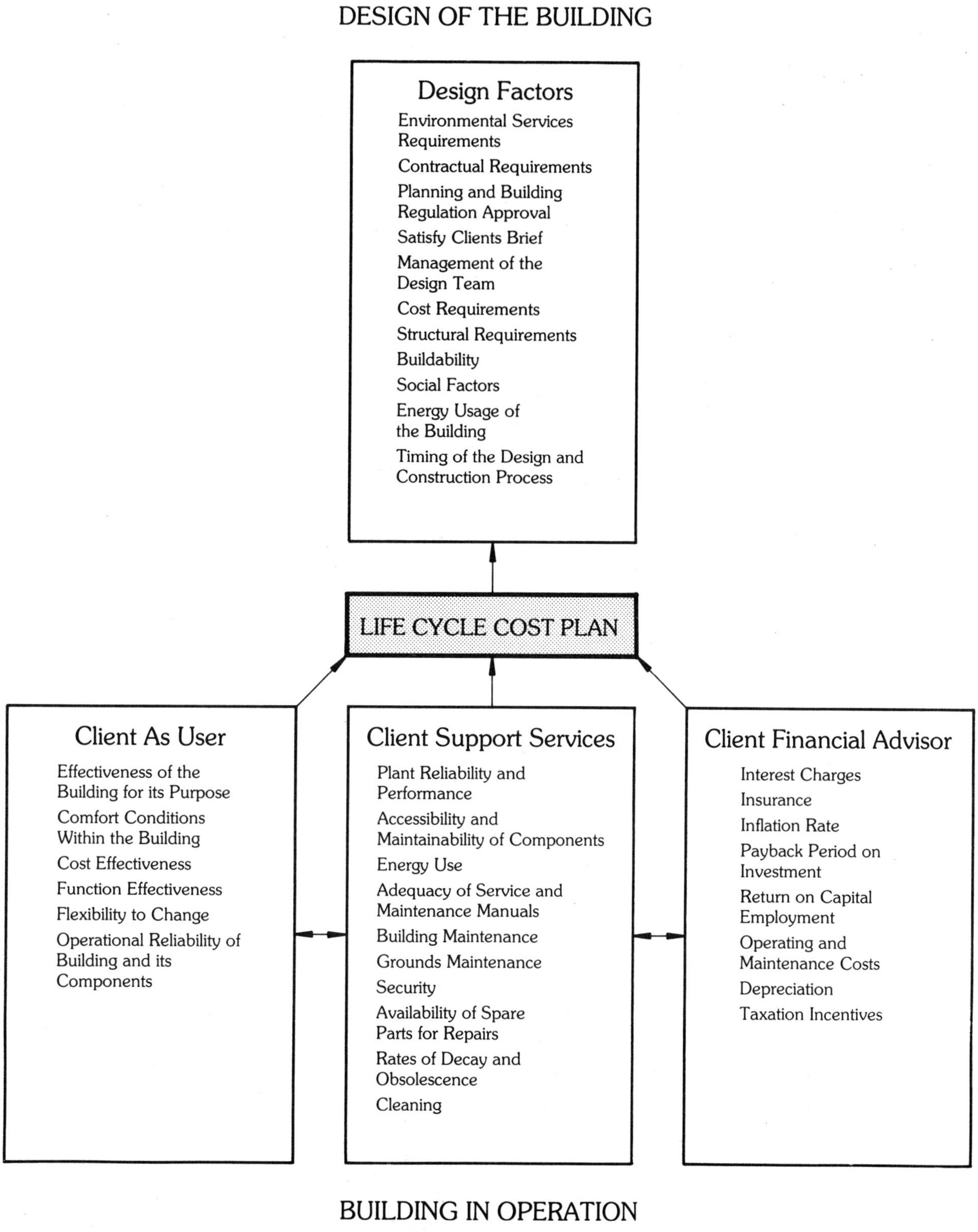

DESIGN OF THE BUILDING

Design Factors

Environmental Services Requirements

Contractual Requirements

Planning and Building Regulation Approval

Satisfy Clients Brief

Management of the Design Team

Cost Requirements

Structural Requirements

Buildability

Social Factors

Energy Usage of the Building

Timing of the Design and Construction Process

LIFE CYCLE COST PLAN

Client As User

Effectiveness of the Building for its Purpose

Comfort Conditions Within the Building

Cost Effectiveness

Function Effectiveness

Flexibility to Change

Operational Reliability of Building and its Components

Client Support Services

Plant Reliability and Performance

Accessibility and Maintainability of Components

Energy Use

Adequacy of Service and Maintenance Manuals

Building Maintenance

Grounds Maintenance

Security

Availability of Spare Parts for Repairs

Rates of Decay and Obsolescence

Cleaning

Client Financial Advisor

Interest Charges

Insurance

Inflation Rate

Payback Period on Investment

Return on Capital Employment

Operating and Maintenance Costs

Depreciation

Taxation Incentives

BUILDING IN OPERATION

Figure 3.2: Relationship between design and building in use

security, and the general day to day running of the building; maintenance personnel who are responsible for the planned and corrective maintenance of the fabric and services; management staff who manage the building (perhaps including the services of a building surveyor who advises on the technical aspects of the overall maintenance policy), and the client's financial staff who provide the technical knowledge on the cost related aspects of the building.

3.5 Overlaying all these groups is the client as the user of the building. Clients are interested in using the building for its design purpose. They often regard the commissioning of a new or newly adapted existing building as a capital cost process and the running costs of the building as a revenue cost process. Both public and private sector clients have historically treated these as separate cost centres, partly because of the loan arrangements in the public sector, and partly because of the different treatment of capital and revenue expenses for taxation purposes in the private sector.

3.6 A further human factor which adds to the complexity is that a number of assumptions must be made about certain items for the running costs to be estimated. For example, the period of building occupancy, the maintenance cycles of certain building elements, and the long term rates of inflation are estimated and uncertainty is inevitable; particularly as the design team has no control over many of the issues. It is essential, therefore, that the assumptions underlying life cycle cost should be clearly stated and qualified to avoid false security in the precision of the numbers that may be used in an analysis.

[handwritten margin notes: Production of information. say on bldg occupancy 10 yrs / 25 yrs / 50 yrs / bldg maintenance 3 yrs / 5 yrs / 10 yrs / using computers — a matter of feeding in the no/years ; PV ; %ages — all tabulated for client]

The components of life cycle cost

3.7 There are several distinct applications of a life cycle cost approach in the construction industry, derived from five questions.

Question 1

What is the total cost commitment of the decision to acquire a particular building or building component?

Question 2

What are the short term running costs associated with the acquisition of a particular building or building component?

Question 3

Which of several options offers the lowest total life cycle cost?

Question 4

What are the running costs of an existing building or building element?

Question 5

How can the running costs on an existing building be reduced?

3.8 Each of these questions can be associated with one of four components of an overall life cycle cost approach:

● Life cycle cost planning: applied to Questions 1 and 3.

● Full year effect costs: applied to Question 2.

● Life cycle cost analysis: applied to Question 4.

● Life cycle cost management: applied to Question 5.

At their simplest, life cycle cost planning and full year effect costs are used during the design phase. Life cycle cost analysis and cost management are used during the occupancy phase when the building is in use.

Life cycle cost planning (LCCP)

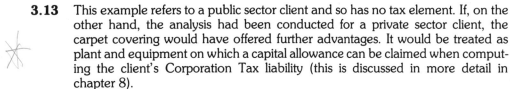

(handwritten margin note:) What about including time cost interest charges incurred during pre & post contract. Cost funding is by short term borrowing. Total Cost Philosophy!

3.9 The first use of LCCP is to identify the total costs of the acquisition of a building or an individual building element. It takes explicit account of initial capital costs and subsequent running costs, and expresses these various costs in a consistent, comparable manner by applying discounting techniques.

3.10 The second use of LCCP is to facilitate the effective choice between various methods of achieving a given objective. Indeed it can be argued that this is the most important aspect of a life cycle cost approach since it will rarely be the case that the quantity surveyor will be presented with only one possibility. Rather, a choice will have to be made between a number of competing options: which design should be chosen? Should there be tiles or carpet? Should the roof be pitched or flat?

3.11 These options are likely to exhibit different initial capital cost and subsequent running cost profiles. LCCP provides a set of techniques to convert this diversity of costs to a single consistent measure of cost effectiveness that makes it easy to compare the various options.

3.12 The output of LCCP and its interpretation in this second use can be illustrated by considering in more detail the floor covering example discussed in chapter 1 (*figure 1.4*). Table 3.A presents the costs of the two options in more detail, and highlights the advantages the carpet covering offers relative to the alternative.

3.13 This example refers to a public sector client and so has no tax element. If, on the other hand, the analysis had been conducted for a private sector client, the carpet covering would have offered further advantages. It would be treated as plant and equipment on which a capital allowance can be claimed when computing the client's Corporation Tax liability (this is discussed in more detail in chapter 8).

3.14 A point worthy of note is that LCCP is dealing with the planning of future costs. The same principles apply to LCCP as to capital cost planning, in that the design team need to be referred to cost targets. The quantity surveyor will set an estimated cost target for each of the chosen categories in the LCCP, which provides a constraint and a measure against which design solutions can be compared. Unlike capital cost planning there is no lowest tender against which to measure the estimating performance of the quantity surveyor. There will be a long time lag before useful running cost data is available for analysis. The temptation must, therefore, be resisted to manipulate the LCCP figures to produce a desired result of low running costs.

3.15 LCCP involves collecting and manipulating data from a variety of sources. It is important that a consistent approach be used in the measurement and presentation of data. For example, if a consulting mechanical and electrical services engineer provides details of the estimated energy requirements for a proposed building for inclusion in the LCCP, it should be clear as to what has been included and excluded in the estimate.

3.16 LCCP does not require any more measurement information than is currently required in capital cost planning. When researching and developing LCCP for this book, it has been borne in mind that unless clients can see considerable financial benefits in LCCP, they will never use the techniques. This means that the professional service should not involve collection of extensive data that are not easily available to the design team.

3.17 It should also be emphasised that LCCP must be objective, comprehensive in scope, responsive to alternative demands, and accomplished in a timely manner. Collectively, the individuals within a surveying practice should become familiar with the data requirements and the analytical techniques employed in LCCP. LCCP has, of course, the ability to handle both initial and continuing costs, reducing them to a common denominator which can be used as part of the decision process. It follows, naturally, that if a decision has no continuing cost consequences, it makes no sense to undertake a life cycle cost plan.

Table 3A: Life cycle cost plan summary calculations

Project:	Floor covering			**Option 1:** Carpet covering		**Option 2:** Wood block covering		**Option 3:**		**Option 4:**	
Location:	New Town										
Date:	1982			**Life cycle:** 25 years		**Life cycle:** 25 years		**Life cycle:**		**Life cycle:**	
Discount rate:	10%										
Costs				Estimated costs	Present value	Estimated costs	Present value	Estimated costs	Present value	Estimated costs	Present value
I:	**Capital costs**										
	Floor screed (£8.99/m²)				9858		9858				
	Carpet (£13.21/m²)				14484						
	Wood block flooring (£9.59/m²)						10509				
	Sub total				24342		20367				
	Contingencies @ 5%				1217		1018				
	Total capital costs				25559		21385				
II: **II.1:**	**Running costs** **Operations costs**	Inflation rate	Inflation adjusted discount factor								
	N/A										
	Total operations costs				–		–				
II.2:	**Maintenance costs annual**										
	Carpet cleaning (£1.86/m²/year)	4%	13.085	2038	26667						
	Wood block cleaning (£3.05/m²/year)	4%	13.085			3340	43704				
	Woodblock refinishing (£1.11/m²/year)	4%	13.085			1222	15990				
	Total maintenance costs (annual)				26667		59694				
II.3:	**Maintenance/ replacement/ alterations (intermittent)**	Year	PV factor								
	Carpet	10	0.5711	14484	8272						
	Carpet	20	0.3268	14484	4733						
	Total maintenance/replacement/ alterations costs				13005		–				
II.4:	**Sundries** N/A										
	Total sundries				–		–				
	Total running costs				39672		59694				
III:	**Additional tax allowances** Public sector client										
	Total additional tax allowances				–		–				
IV:	**Salvage and residuals** N/A										
	Total salvage and residuals				–		–				
	Total net present value of life cycle costs				65231		81079				
	Annual equivalent value of life cycle costs				7187		8933				

Full year effect costs (FYEC)

3.18 Sometimes clients will wish to know, at the design stage, the actual running costs of a proposed building in the short term. Normally an estimate of the running cost for a period of one to three years is provided. This estimate is the FYEC. Future costs are not discounted, but allowance is made in the calculations for the effect of inflation. In essence the client is given information on the likely short term running costs of a design choice.

3.19 Many public and private sector clients will use FYEC for budgeting purposes. In practical terms, FYEC is the estimated real expenditure for either new or existing buildings, usually expressed as an annual amount.

Life cycle cost analysis (LCCA)

3.20 LCCA involves the collection of information on the running costs and performance of occupied buildings. In order for the cost data to be meaningful, LCCA must be linked with details about the physical performance, and qualitative characteristics of the building. *Figure 3.3* shows in simple diagrammatic form the types of information collected within the four data areas.

3.21 The main use of LCCA is as a management tool intended to identify the actual costs incurred in operating buildings (or, indeed, any durable assets). Since LCCA forms part of overall cost management, it should not be thought of as an end in itself. Rather, by identifying the main items of expenditure incurred in the occupation and maintenance of buildings, LCCA will generate an historical data base. This data base can then be used to highlight areas in which cost savings might be achieved in the design of new buildings, in the operation of existing buildings, and in the choice of individual building components.

3.22 The primary objective of LCCA is to relate running cost and performance data and to provide feedback to the design team about the running costs of occupied buildings. In order for this to be effective a system must be developed to enable the data to be collected in a structured fashion. In the case of a new building,

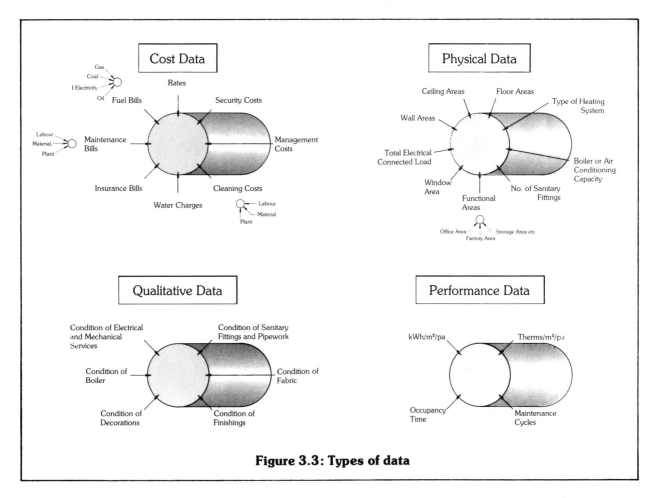

Figure 3.3: Types of data

many of the physical and performance data will be available to the design team. However, where an existing building has been occupied for some considerable time it is likely that the data will not be collected in a fashion suitable for LCCA. The client is unlikely to keep records on the performance and qualitative aspects of his building. Information is likely to be available in the form of invoices on cost areas such as fuel, rates and insurances. It is probable that the occupied building will need to be measured and calculations undertaken to ascertain the physical performance.

3.23 In simple terms, the following questions at least should be asked:

- What is the building type?

Then, for each building:

- Where is it located?   *Building shape — refer Peter Brandon research on shape/cost*
- Are there any drawings available?
- What is the breakdown of the functional floor areas?
- What is the general construction?   *Use of building eg.computers as in CEGB in Avm see 'Building' reports*
- What is its general condition?
- When was it built?
- What running cost information is available?
- What is the condition of the individual elements (fabric, frame, finishes, etc.)?
- What are the periods of occupancy?
- What is the maintenance policy?
- Has the building been modernised?
- What type is the heating installation?

3.24 Quite clearly, a much more extensive list of questions could be detailed, but the major consideration is the desire for simplicity. It is pointless to capture data which will not be used in some meaningful fashion. Simplicity is paramount in the design of any system.

3.25 LCCA deals with historical costs and does not involve discounting. When a number of LCCAs have been undertaken for different projects it must be remembered that they relate to cost data for different buildings, in different locations, with different occupancy, at a fixed period of time. No two buildings will have identical running costs, nor will the running costs for any specific building be the same from year to year.

3.26 Many possible benefits will be lost if the building's performance and costs of ownership are not monitored throughout its life. It is important to the design team that there is feedback on the cost and performance of the building in use. In practical terms, this has proved difficult in the past for a number of reasons.

Refer USA system of fee scale

- The design teams must be paid a professional fee to undertake their work and clients have not commissioned professionals from the design team to life cycle cost analyse their buildings.
- There has been no standardised systematic approach to the collection of performance and cost data for occupied buildings which would enable a useful analysis to be undertaken.
- There is a long time lag between design, occupation, and availability of reliable data on running costs.

Nevertheless, LCCA must form a central part of any meaningful life cycle cost approach to buildings.

Life cycle cost management (LCCM)

3.27 LCCM is a derivative of LCCA. It identifies those areas in which running costs detailed by LCCA might be reduced, either by a change in operating practice, or by changing the relevant system.

3.28 LCCM is intended:

- To establish where performance differs from the LCCP projections, why the differences occur, whether they are significant, and whether current performance could be altered.

- To make recommendations on more efficient utilisation of the building.

- To provide information on asset lives and reliability factors for accounting purposes.

- To assist in the establishment of a maintenance policy for the building.

- To give taxation advice on building related items.

3.29 Essentially, LCCM is designed to answer the following types of question.

- *Should the floor covering be changed from tiles to carpet?*

- *Should the office area windows be double glazed to reduce heating costs?*

3.30 In this sense, LCCM is to existing buildings and building systems what LCCP is to new buildings and building systems. It is worth restating (see chapter 1), that this is one of the most important areas for the application of life cycle cost techniques. Buildings may be expected to endure and be used for many years, during which time design decisions may need to be changed and new options considered.

Life cycle costing and quantity surveying practice

3.31 In order for life cycle costing to be adopted by quantity surveyors, it must prove itself to be economically viable for clients, surveyors and professional advisers. Furthermore, it must be seen as a practical tool that enhances existing professional skills and relates in some way to the tasks currently performed by surveyors.

3.32 The temptation to dismiss life cycle costing techniques as being merely costs-in-use techniques with different terminology must be resisted. Life cycle costing brings together the costs-in-use concept and links it to the formal structure of cost planning and long term ownership costs.

3.33 Table 3.B shows the relationship between the initial budget price forecast, the cost plan, the bill of quantities, and the final account for a building project. As the design develops more information becomes available about a building and more detailed measurement is undertaken. The life cycle cost approach uses as its basis the measurement information from the traditional quantity surveying process.

Table 3B: Life cycle costing and quantity surveying practice

Traditional quantity surveying tasks	Measurement	Life cycle costing tasks
Forecasting budget price based upon outline proposals	Approximate superficial gross floor areas	Forecast target prices for life cycle cost categories
Cost plan based upon sketch and scheme design	Areas of elemental categories	Detailed life cycle cost plan Full year effect costs considered in life cycle cost categories Budget forecast for capital allowances
Bills of quantities based upon detail design	Detailed measurements and prime cost and provisional sums	Target cost checks made on the life cycle cost plan and the full year effect costs
Final account at completion of project	Detailed measurements	Life cycle cost management targets established Taxation account detailing capital allowances for building, plant and equipment

A life cycle costing system

3.34 To convert theoretical concepts into practical reality requires a formal system. In the same way that cost planning uses elemental categories, so the total cost approach to a project uses life cycle cost categories. It must be emphasized that any system of life cycle cost categories is merely a filing system; a series of pigeonholes designed as reminders of possible costs to be included. Whether these costs are initial capital costs or costs incurred on a continuing or cyclical basis during the life of a building, they are all costs that arise from and are affected by design decisions with respect to the building.

3.35 The major life cycle cost categories are as follows.

- Capital costs (including land and construction costs).
- Operations costs (including cleaning, energy, etc.).
- Maintenance costs (annual).
- Maintenance, replacement and alterations costs (intermittent).
- Sundries.
- Salvage and residuals.

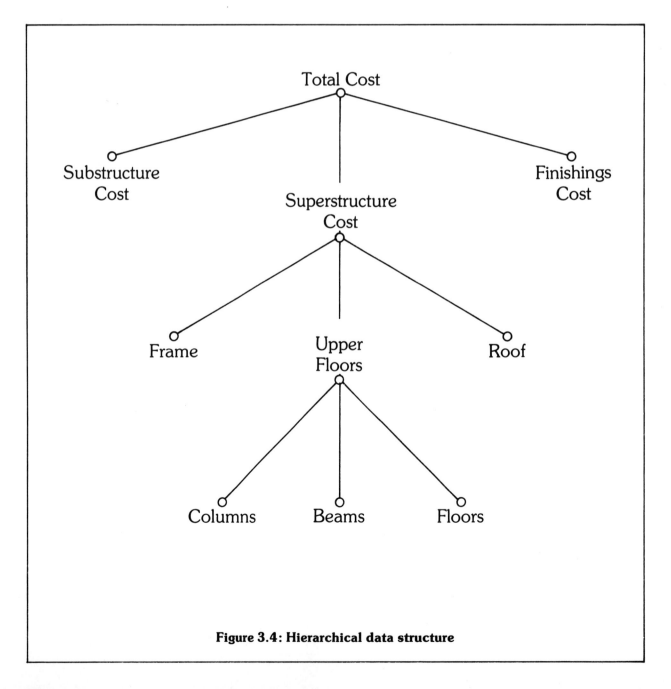

Figure 3.4: Hierarchical data structure

The concept of levels for life cycle cost

3.36 In developing life cycle cost for quantity surveyors, it is recognised that the techniques involve the manipulation of large amounts of data. These data can be grouped into a hierarchical structure such as the one shown in *figure 3.4*.

3.37 The data structure is analogous to the hierarchical library classification based upon the traditional 'tree of knowledge'. Items are classified to successive sub-divisions by consistent reference to a single common attribute at each stage. When this concept is related to life cycle cost categories it is easiest to think in terms of levels. For example, *figure 3.5* illustrates a structure of levels for maintenance. At level 1, maintenance as an all-embracing item for the whole building is considered. Level 2 looks at one element associated with maintenance, in this case the finishes, while level 3 further sub-divides this element into the appropriate types of finishes. The whole concept should be self-explanatory; what is important is that the levels can fit a number of tasks associated with LCCA, LCCP and LCCM.

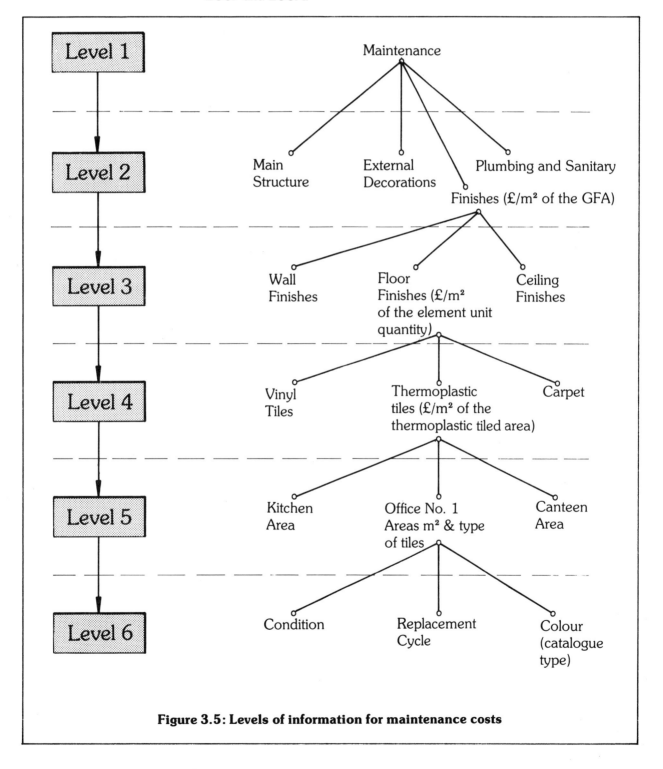

Figure 3.5: Levels of information for maintenance costs

3.38 If a very early design were being evaluated for an LCCP it is unlikely that any analysis beyond level 1 would be undertaken. As more information becomes available the maintenance item would be analysed at level 2. The point of entry into the levels is dependent solely upon the extent of the information available. Levels 5 and 6 are mainly involved in structuring a maintenance management programme. For example, at level 6 by using an effective LCCM it is possible to identify when the thermoplastic tiling in an office is due for replacement.

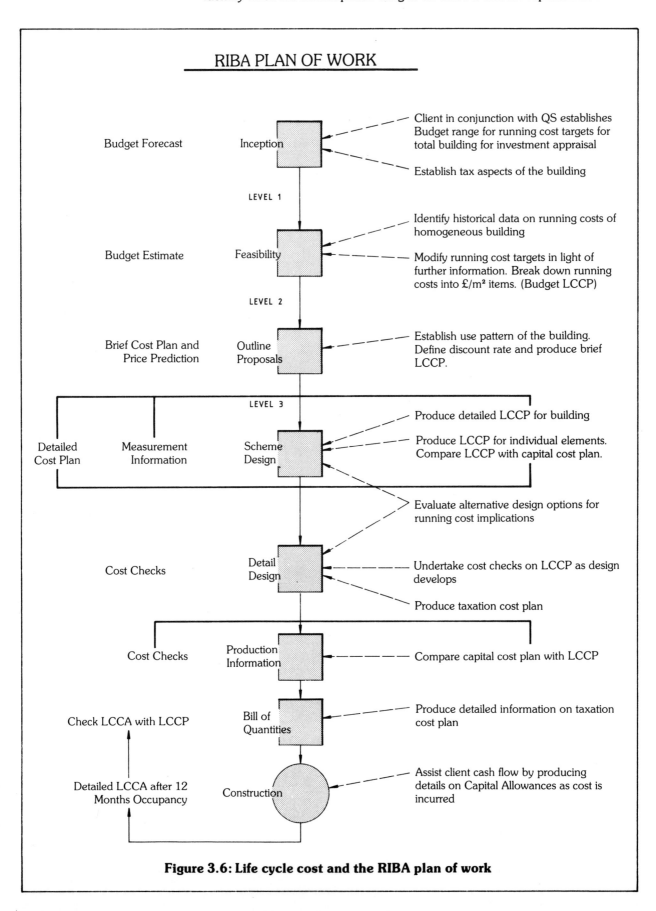

Figure 3.6: Life cycle cost and the RIBA plan of work

3.39 The problem must be seen in the context of what it would cost to capture this information and why the information is needed. All clients are involved in expenditure on the running costs of their buildings, and therefore the expenditure must be budgeted and planned in some way. Hence the need for a structured approach to life cycle costing.

3.40 In developing the items in the various levels, attention has been paid to the Building Maintenance Cost Information Service and Building Cost Information Service categories, and to the Chartered Institute of Public Finance and Accounting and Department of the Environment maintenance categories. Further, *figure 3.6* shows how life cycle costing operates in relation to the RIBA Plan of Work. As the design develops it is possible to move from an LCCP based upon level 1 to a more detailed approach at level 3. The conventional cost planning sequence is shown on the left hand side of the diagram.

3.41 LCCP may be used at any stage in the design process. This aspect of life cycle

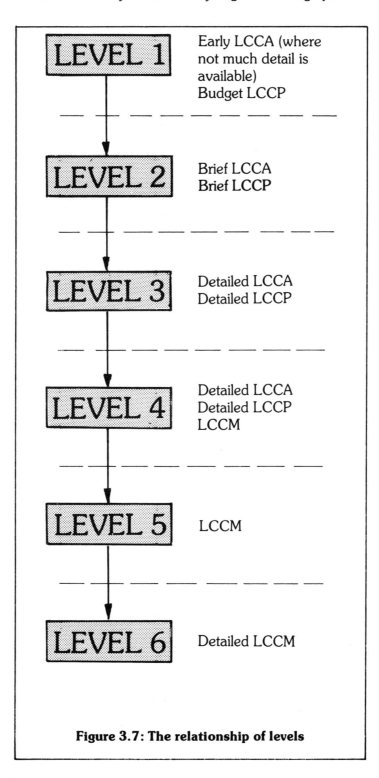

Figure 3.7: The relationship of levels

costing is all about decision-making, whether this be for the selection of alternative glazing types or for establishing the running costs at the inception stage of a complete building. The technique can be useful even if it is not used throughout the design process.

3.42   The relationship between the levels and LCCA, LCCP and LCCM is shown in *figure 3.7*. The terms early, brief, budget and detailed have been used to expand the notion of the purpose of LCCA, LCCP and LCCM.

Life cycle cost categories

3.43   The appendix to this chapter details the life cycle cost categories developed from level 1 to level 3. This appendix has a number of uses.

● It can act as a checklist of items.

● It can form the basis of categories for an LCCP or LCCM when used in conjunction with measurement information.

● Cost information can be recorded under the various categories when compiling an LCCA.

3.44   It must be emphasised that the list is more suggestive than exhaustive. There are numerous items that have not been included, mainly because it is not feasible to cover every eventuality in one comprehensive list.

3.45   Many costs will be incurred annually but some will be intermittent. For example, under the maintenance section there will be planned/preventive maintenance, corrective maintenance (repairs), upgrading work, adaptation and alteration work. The list must, therefore, be modified to suit each user. Some owners may wish to go down to the level of detail that identifies repairs caused by vandalism, whereas other owners may require only maintenance costs at level 1.

Chapter 3: Appendix

Level 1	Level 2		Level 3	
1. Capital costs	1A	Land		
	1B	Fees on acquisition	B1	legal
			B2	estate agents
			B3	solicitor
			B4	stamp duty
			B5	rights of way
			B6	rights of light
			B7	party wall awards
			B8	other
	1C	Design team professional fees	C1	architect
			C2	town planner
			C3	quantity surveyor
			C4	structural engineer
			C5	civil engineer
			C6	mechanical services engineer
			C7	electrical engineer
			C8	landscape architect
			C9	interior designer
			C10	graphic designer
			C11	project manager
			C12	clerk of works
			C13	building surveyor
			C14	land surveyor
			C15	energy consultant
			C16	other
	1D	Demolition & site clearance (if applicable)		

Level 1	Level 2		Level 3	
	1E	Construction price for building work		
	1F	Cost of statutory consents	F1 F2 F3 F4 F5 F6	outline & detail planning approval building regulation approval district surveyor listed building consent conservation area consent other
	1G	Finance for land purchase & during construction	G1 G2 G3 G4	short term medium term long term other
	1H	Development Land Tax (if applicable)		
	1I	Capital Gains Tax (if applicable)		
	1J	Value Added Tax (if applicable)		
	1K	Furnishings	K1 K2 K3 K4	carpets curtains furniture other
	1L	Removal charges		
	1M	Disruption cost (loss of product-ivity & profits including any double overheads)		
	1N	Other capital costs (e.g. plant & equipment)		
	1O	Commissioning expenses		
	1P	Decanting charges (cost of any tempor-ary accommodation & disruption)		
	1Q	Other		
2. Finance costs	2A	Finance during period of intended occupation	A1 A2 A3 A4	short term medium term long term other
	2B	Loan charges (public sector)		
3. Operation costs	3A	Fuel (where possible apportion fuel bill to appropriate categories) (i) gas (ii) oil (iii) coal (iv) electricity (v) other	A1 A2 A3 A4 A5 A6 A7 A8 A9	heating cooling hot water ventilation lifts, escalators & conveyors lighting building equipment & appliances special user plant & equipment other

Level 1	Level 2		Level 3	
	3B	Cleaning	B1	internal surfaces
			B1(i)	user
			B1(ii)	circulation
			B2	external surfaces
			B2(i)	windows
			B2(ii)	external fabric
			B3	lighting
			B4	laundry & towel cabinets
			B5	external works
			B6	refuse disposal
			B7	chimneys & flues
			B8	other
	3C	Rates	C1	general rates
			C2	water rates
			C3	effluents & drainage charge
			C4	empty rates
			C5	other
	3D	Insurances	D1	property insurance
			D2	mechanical & electrical services/ combined engineering
			D3	boilers
			D4	electric motors & pumps
			D5	fixtures & fittings
			D6	public liability
			D7	employer's liability
			D8	loss of profits or rent receivable
			D9	special perils
			D10	lifts, sprinklers & boilers statutory inspections
			D11	other
	3E	Security and health	E1	security services
			E2	pest control
			E3	dust control
			E4	other
	3F	Staff	F1	porterage
			F2	caretaker
			F3	commissionaire
			F4	lift attendant
			F5	gardening
			F6	uniforms
			F7	other
	3G	Management and administration of the building	G1	builder manager/occupancy manager
			G2	plan manager/engineer
			G3	building management consultancy fees
			G4	telephone charges
			G5	stationery and postage
			G6	other
	3H	Land charges	H1	ground rent
			H2	chief rent
			H3	easements
			H4	other
4. Maintenance costs Main structure	4A	Main structure	A1	substructure
			A2	frame
			A3	upper floors
			A4	roof structure/roof covering & rainwater drainage
			A5	stair structure/stair finish/ stair balustrade
			A6	external walls
			A7	windows, external doors & ironmongery
			A8	internal walls & partitions
			A9	internal doors & ironmongery
			A10	other

Level 1	Level 2		Level 3	
Decorations	4B	External decorations		
	4C	Internal decorations	C1 C2 C3 C4 C5	wall decorations ceiling decorations fittings joinery other
Finishes/fixtures/ fittings	4D	Finishes/fixtures/ fittings	D1 D2 D3 D4 D5 D6 D7 D8	internal wall finishes internal floor finishes internal ceiling finishes internal suspended ceilings fixtures fittings curtains & furnishings other
Plumbing, mechanical & electrical services	4E	Plumbing & sanitary services	E1 E2 E3 E4 E5	sanitary appliances services equipment disposal installation/internal drainage cold & hot water services/ water mains supply other
	4F	Heat source	F1 F2 F3	boilers, controls, plant & equipment fuel storage & supply other
	4G	Space heating & air treatment	G1 G2 G3 G4 G5 G6 G7 G8 G9 G10 G11 G12	water and/or steam (heating only) ducted warm air (heating only) electricity (heating only) local heating other heating systems heating with ventilation (air heated locally) heating with ventilation (air heated centrally) heating with cooling (air heated locally) heating with cooling (air heated centrally) solar collectors heat pumps other
	4H	Ventilating systems	H1 H2 H3 H4 H5 H6 H7	ventilation supply kitchen extract fume extract dust collection smoke extract car parking extract other
	4I	Electrical installations	I1 I2 I3 I4 I5 I6	electric source mains electric power supplies & lighting electric lighting fittings (includes re-lamping) emergency lighting external lighting other
	4J	Gas installations	J1 J2 J3	town and natural gas services distribution pipework to appliances & equipment other
	4K	Lift & conveyor installations	K1 K2 K3 K4	lift installations escalators hoists other
	4L	Communication installations	L1 L2 L3 L4	fire & theft warning installations visual & audio installations telephones other

Level 1	Level 2		Level 3	
	4M	Special installations/ protective installations	M1	fire protection
			M2	refrigeration equipment
			M3	kitchen equipment
			M4	laundry equipment
			M5	incinerators & flues
			M6	water heaters
			M7	hand driers
			M8	window cleaning equipment
			M9	refuse disposal equipment
			M10	water pumps
			M11	lightning protection
			M12	Mechanical or electrical equipment associated with the building occupier's occupation
			M13	specialist equipment for a computer installation
			M14	dock levellers to loading bays
			M15	sewer pumps
			M16	other
External works	4N	External works	N1	repairs & decorations
			N2	roads & paved areas
			N3	boundaries
			N4	external services
			N5	drainage
			N6	fencing
			N7	other
	4P	Gardening		
5. Occupancy costs				
6. Sundries	6A	Energy conservation measures		
	6B	Equipment associated with the building occupier's occupation	B1	safes
			B2	racking to a warehouse
			B3	other
	6C	Internal planting		
7. Salvage and Residuals	7A	Resale value	A1	building
			A2	land
			A3	plant and equipment
			A4	other
	7B	Related costs	B1	demolition and site clearance
			B2	disposal fee and charges
			B3	other
	7C	Capital Gains Tax		

Chapter **4**

Key Points

- The use of the pay-back period is not an adequate method of appraisal for life cycle cost purposes (para. 4.6).

- Money at a future date is not equivalent to the same sum of money now (para. 4.8). Future money is converted into its equivalent in today's money by discounting (para. 4.11).

- The discount rate is the time value of money (para. 4.11).

- All costs and revenues associated with a particular option should be identified, and must take into account the impact of taxation and investment incentives (para. 4.22).

- Future cost savings generated by a current cash outlay will have to be greater as the discount rate is greater (para. 4.25).

- The real, long-term cost of borrowing money in the market place should be chosen as the discount rate (para. 4.27).

- The discount rate will vary with the source of funding (para. 4.29). If funding is solely by retained earnings the discount rate should be the cost of equity finance adjusted for tax savings (para. 4.31).

- Discounting methods are used to rank options (para. 4.36).

- Either an absolute or incremental approach can be used for discounting (para. 4.37). It is recommended that the absolute approach be used in life cycle cost calculations (para. 4.43).

- Where alternatives have different project lives the cost of each alternative should be expressed as an annual equivalent. The least cost alternative is that with the lowest annual equivalent (para. 4.45).

- Net present value comparison is preferred to internal rate of return comparison as the method of appraisal for life cycle cost purposes (para. 4.54).

- Present value calculations must take inflation into account (para. 4.55).

- In the absence of better information it is recommended that a real test discount rate of 4% be used (para. 4.57).

- Where the expected inflation rate exceeds the cost of capital, present value calculations should be performed using a net inflation rate (para. 4.63).

- When estimates are uncertain, calculations should be subjected to a sensitivity analysis (para. 4.71).

4

The time value of money

Introduction

4.1 The four components (LCCA, LCCP, LCCM, FYEC) of a life cycle cost approach, as identified in chapter 3, have one essential common feature. In order to answer the questions on which they are based it will be necessary to express, in common terms, cash flows that arise at different times. The surveyor must, therefore, have available a set of techniques that will convert future cash outlays to their current equivalent. This chapter outlines such a set of techniques and shows how it can be used.

4.2 At this practical level, life cycle cost is an application of *investment appraisal*. It is, therefore, useful to show why one commonly used method of investment appraisal, pay-back period, is not appropriate for life cycle cost.

4.3 The essence of investment appraisal using pay-back period is to identify those options for which revenues most quickly cover the initial capital costs. A first complication in using this technique for life cycle cost comparisons is that it will be necessary to generate time series of revenues rather than costs. Ways can be found for doing this, but nevertheless several other fundamental failings of pay-back period appraisal remain. These are best identified by example.

Example 1:

Two design options for a replacement heating system with cost profiles are shown as follows.

Option A
i.	installation cost	£20,000
ii.	annual savings on existing heating costs	£5,000
iii.	expected life of new system	5 years

Option B
i.	installation cost	£28,000
ii.	annual savings on existing heating costs	£5,500
iii.	expected life of new system	12 years

The pay-back periods are:

Option A = 20,000 ÷ 5,000 = 4 years

Option B = 28,000 ÷ 5,500 = 5.1 years

4.4 Option A would be chosen on the pay-back criterion, but a strong argument can be made in favour of Option B. The essential points are, firstly, pay-back ignores all costs and revenues outside the pay-back period. Thus no account is taken of the fact that Option A will have to be replaced after 5 years, with consequent additional installation costs.

4.5 Secondly, as will be clarified later, a sum of money received or spent today is not equivalent to the same sum of money received or spent next year, or in some years' time. This feature, *the time value of money*, is ignored by pay-back period methods of investment appraisal.

4.6 It must be concluded that pay-back period is not an adequate method for life cycle cost purposes. A method of appraisal is needed which takes account of all present and future cost flows and expresses these costs in a uniform, time-independent manner.

Discounting

4.7   This section begins by investigating in more detail the proposition that 'money today' is in some sense different from 'money tomorrow', and then shows how present and future money flows can be expressed in common terms.

4.8   For example, an individual who is given the choice of receiving £1,000 now or in a year's time, would clearly choose to receive the money now. On the other hand, if offered the choice of settling a £1,000 debt now or next year he would choose to pay the £1,000 next year. In the former case some return can be expected on the investment, such as the return on a bank or building society deposit, while interest payments can accrue on the money retained. The assumption is that there is no interest payable on the debt.

4.9   Given that money at a future date is not equivalent to the same sum of money now, a central problem in life cycle costing is to reduce cash expenditures and receipts that arise at different points in time to a common base. It is, therefore, necessary to identify a meaningful 'exchange rate' between money now and money at a future date. This exchange rate is referred to as the *time value of money*.

4.10   Consider the case in which an individual, having received £1,000 now, can reinvest this sum at a net of tax, risk free return of 5% per annum compound, say by depositing it in a bank. At the end of the first year the £1,000 will have grown to £1,050, after two years it will have grown to £1,102.50 and so on. It can be assumed that this 5% return represents the individual's best available use for the additional funds. In such a case he should value £1,050 in a year's time, £1,102.50 in two years' time, etc., as equivalent to £1,000 now. Put another way, in this example the investor is exchanging money one year hence for money today at a rate of £1.05 for £1. Thus any sum £x to be received one year hence would be valued by him at only £x/1.05 today. Similarly, £x received two years hence would be valued at £x/1.1025 or £x/1.05², today. In general, £x received in *t* years' time with rate of interest *r*% is worth today, a present value (PV) of:

$$PV \text{ of } x = £x/(1 + r)^t \tag{4.I}$$

The present value factor (PVF) by which a cash flow of £1 in year *t* can be expressed in its present value is, from equation (4.I):

$$PVF = 1/(1 + r)^t \tag{4.II}$$

4.11   This process by which future money is converted into its equivalent in present money is called *discounting* and derives its name from the fact that future money is being reduced (discounted) to its current money equivalent, in other words to its *present value*. The rate at which future money is discounted, the discount rate, is conventionally taken to represent the time value of money. *Figure 4.1* illustrates the effects of alternative discount rates on the present value of £1,000 received at varying times in the future.

4.12   As can be seen from *figure 4.1*, the choice of discount rate will have a significant effect on present value calculations. Consideration must, therefore, be given to the criteria on which the discount rate should be chosen. This is discussed in some detail below. In order to make that discussion more meaningful, however, it is first necessary to illustrate the main principles of discounting.

Discounting methods

4.13   The ideas underlying discounting and the main components necessary for effective life cycle costing using discounting techniques are best illustrated by a series of simple examples. These examples will illustrate different aspects of discounting methods, but they have one common feature that must be noted at this point. Since the objective of discounting is to produce a present value it follows that this present value will relate to current prices. It is to be expected, however, that costs will escalate over time – it was noted in previous chapters that this is one major reason why a life cycle cost approach is now of vital concern to the

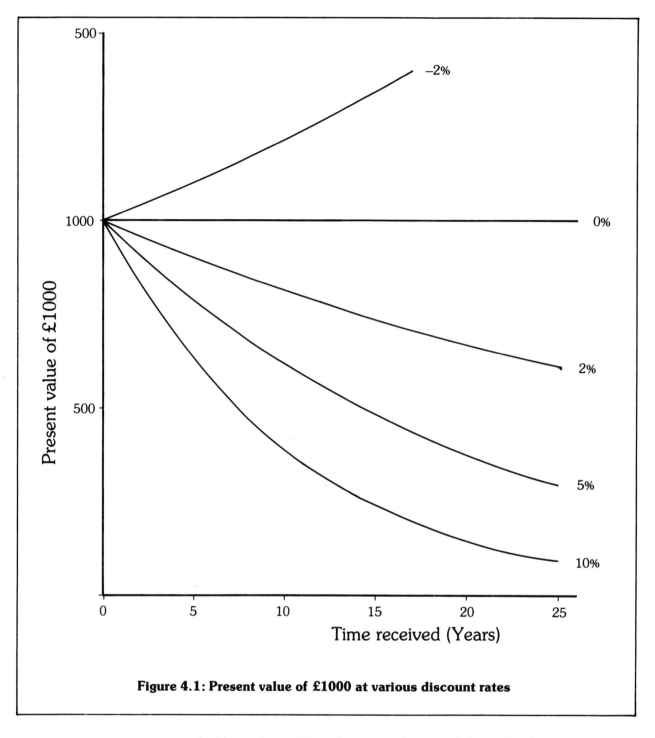

Figure 4.1: Present value of £1000 at various discount rates

building industry. When discounting future cash flows, therefore, account must be taken of the effects of inflation. The principles on which this should be done are discussed in detail below. It is sufficient at this stage to note the simple arithmetic calculations that should be made prior to applying the discounting techniques. Consider a situation in which costs associated with a particular project are expected to escalate at 10% and the long-term market cost of borrowing the finance for that project is 15.5%. Then the net of inflation discount rate is given by:

$$\left(\frac{1.155}{1.10} - 1\right) \times 100 = 5\%$$

More generally, if the expected escalation (inflation) rate is $i\%$ and the long-term market cost of capital is $d\%$, the net of inflation discount rate is given by:

$$r = \left(\frac{1+i}{1+d} - 1\right) \times 100$$

This principle is illustrated by example 2:

Example 2

It is projected that an additional £10,000 investment in a building's heating and ventilating system will reduce annual fuel costs (at current prices) by £2,000. If it is expected to own the facility for 5 years, and the additional investment can be expected to increase the resale value by £2,000, would the investment be worthwhile?

It is assumed that the rate of Corporation Tax is 50%, that the investment qualifies for 100% first year capital allowance, and that this allowance will be taken totally in the first year.

The total net of tax cash saving is £7,000, but this is received over a period of 5 years, and so must be converted, i.e. discounted, to its present value.

On the assumption that the investment can be financed by borrowing at 15.5% interest compounded annually and that fuel costs are expected to escalate by 10% per annum, the effective discount rate (allowing for inflation) is 5% (1.155 ÷ 1.10 = 1.05), and the present value of the net of tax fuel costs savings and increased resale value is:

$$\frac{£1000}{1.05} + \frac{£1000}{1.05^2} + \frac{£1000}{1.05^3} + \frac{£1000}{1.05^4} + \frac{£1000}{1.05^5} + \frac{£2000}{1.05^5} =$$

$$952 + 907 + 864 + 823 + 784 + 1568 = £5898$$

while the current net of tax cash outlay is £5,000. The net present value (NPV) of the investment is, therefore, £898. Since this is positive, the investment is worthwhile.

4.14 This example can be used to illustrate several other features of discounting. First, the example is a particular illustration of a general principle. The NPV of any stream of costs and revenue occurring over a life cycle of N years is given by the general formula:

$$NPV = (R_0 - C_0) + \frac{(R_1 - C_1)}{1 + r} + \frac{(R_2 - C_2)}{(1 + r)^2} + \cdots$$

$$+ \frac{(R_N - C_N)}{(1 + r)^N} = \sum_{t=0}^{N} \frac{(R_t - C_t)}{(1 + r)^t} \qquad (4.II)$$

4.15 Second, the calculations can, and preferably should, be presented in tabular form as in table 4.A.

Table 4A: Discounted cash flow: example 2

Year	Cash flows					Present value factor @ 5%	Annuity factor† @ 5%	Present value I (5×6)	Present value of annuity	Present value II
	Outflow	Tax component	Inflow	Tax* component	Net (1+2+3+4)					
	(1)	(2)	(3)	(4)	(5)	(6)	(7)	(8)	(9)	(10)
0	−10,000	5000	−	−	−5000	1.000		−5000		−5000
1	−	−	2000	−1000	1000	.952		952		
2	−	−	2000	−1000	1000	.907		907		
3	−	−	2000	−1000	1000	.864	4.329	864	4329	4329
4	−	−	2000	−1000	1000	.823		823		
5	−	−	4000	−1000	3000	.784		2352		1568
Net present value								**+898**		**+897**

* The tax component is negative since a reduction in fuel costs reduced a tax deductable element. No tax element is included in respect of the increased resale value.
† See text.

4.16 The third feature is illustrated in table 4.A. All cash flows are assumed to arise at the end of the year in which they are incurred or received. Thus the fuel cost savings are assumed to accrue to the firm at the end of years 1, 2, etc. This assumption is not vital, of course. An identical analysis could be performed assuming quarterly, monthly or even daily expenditures and receipts, or on the assumption that all cash flows occur in mid-year. The complications so introduced to the calculations, however, do not in general justify the additional accuracy gained thereby. If the viability of a project is significantly affected by whether cash flows are annual or quarterly, it should be treated with some suspicion!

4.17 The fourth feature of discounting is also illustrated in table 4.a. Calculations can be simplified, and calculating time saved, whenever a project has a number of years of constant net income. The value of the fuel savings in years 1-5 can be treated as a 5 year annuity. Consulting annuity tables, sometimes referred to as 'present value of £1 per annum' tables, the present value of £1 per annum for 5 years at 5% is £4.329. This is identical, allowing for slight rounding errors, to the sum of the five present value factors in table 4.A.

4.18 The present value of an annuity (PVA) of £1 for N years discounted at r% is:

$$PVA = \frac{(1 + r)^N - 1}{(1 + r)^N \cdot r}$$

$$(4.III)$$

4.19 The annuity factor gives the present value of the annuity at the beginning of year 1; that is, at the base date. This is particularly important where regular net cash flows begin other than in year 1, as in example 3.

Example 3

As example 2, except that fuel savings in year 1 are only £1,800. Calculations are detailed in table 4.B.

Table 4B: Annuity beginning other than in year 1: example 3

Year	Cash flows			Present value factor @ 5%	Annuity factor @ 5%	Present value
	Total	Tax component	Net cash flow			
0	−10000	5000	−5000	1.000		−5000
1	1800	900	900	.952		857
2	2000	−1000	1000			
3	2000	−1000	1000		3.546 × .952 = 3.376	3376
4	2000	−1000	1000			
5	2000	−1000	1000			
	2000		2000	.784		1568
Net present value						**+801**

The annuity factor now refers to an annuity for 4 years, and since the annuity begins in year 2, gives the present value of the annuity as if it arose at the beginning of year 2. This is exactly equivalent to its arising at the end of year 1. Hence, to get the present value of this sum at the base date, it is merely necessary to multiply it by the one year discount factor (0.952).

4.20 In the original example, the effects on the project's viability of changes in the key elements of the calculations can be examined. Table 4.C presents the NPV for example 2 under a series of different discount rates and project lives, and identifies those conditions under which the project should and should not be accepted.

Table 4C: Net present value with different discount rates and project lives: example 2

Project life	Discount rate (%)					
	2	4	5	6	8	10
3	−232	−447	−549	−647	−835	−1011
4	656	340	192	49	−218	− 464
5	1525	1096	897	706	355	33
6	2377	1822	1568	1327	883	483
7	3214	2522	2208	1912	1372	894

4.21 Similar calculations can be performed to illustrate the effects of assumptions regarding the probable fuel savings, resale value, or initial cost of the project. This amounts to a sensitivity analysis of the project. Sensitivity analysis will be considered in more detail below; it is a technique intended to identify those elements of a project which have the greatest impact on the project's viability. In looking at table 4.C, it is necessary to know only that the project life is at least 4 years for it to be viable, as long as it is reasonably certain that the projected cash flows are accurate, and that the effective (inflation adjusted) discount rate is 5%.

The main components of discounting

I: The time stream of costs and revenues

4.22 It was noted above that the objective of discounting and of discounted cash flow, when applied to life cycle cost, is to express future flows of cash in their present value. A central component of the analysis, therefore, is the estimated time stream of expenditures and receipts. It is imperative that all costs and revenues associated with a particular option be identified. In addition, these costs and revenues must take into account such considerations as the impact of taxation and investment incentives. This should on the whole be straightforward for corporate taxation, but where investment incentives, for example, are available as a reduction in the tax liability of corporate profits, calculations will be somewhat more complex.

4.23 The costs and revenues that are appropriate will depend upon the individual study. If alternative design options are being compared, for example the plan shape or number of storeys for a particular building, it will be necessary to perform a full life cycle cost for each option prior to comparison. On the other hand, if different floor covering options are being compared, an incremental approach might be adopted. One option could be chosen as the base and, as in examples 2 and 3 above, others evaluated in terms of their incremental effects on installation costs, running costs and resale value.

4.24 This may sound reasonably straightforward, but will often be quite complicated in practice. For example, different glazing options will affect not only installation and energy costs through their differential effects on insulation, but possibly also costs of air conditioning, lighting, and cleaning. Effective evaluation of the time stream of costs and revenues requires, therefore, an equally effective view of the building as a complex and interactive system.

II: The discount rate

4.25 The second major component of life cycle cost is the choice of discount rate, that is, the choice of the time value of money. Indeed, it can be argued that the discount rate is one of the critical variables in the analysis, in that the decision as to whether to proceed with a particular investment project will be crucially affected by the choice of discount rate. It has already been seen that the process of discounting future cash to give its present value reduces the present value of future receipts, and reduces the present cost of future outlays. What this implies is that the future cost savings (or future cash receipts) generated by a current cash outlay will have to be greater the greater is the discount rate. This is

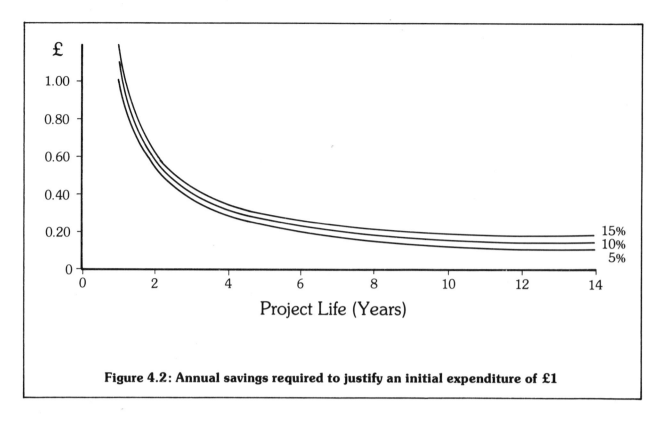

Figure 4.2: Annual savings required to justify an initial expenditure of £1

illustrated in *figure 4.2* which illustrates the annual savings required to justify an extra initial expenditure of £1.

4.26 For example, a situation may arise in which a choice has to be made between alternative floor coverings for a new office. These coverings are expected to have the same life, 10 years, but covering B has a higher purchase price and lower annual cleaning costs than covering A. For covering B to be preferred the annual saving in cleaning costs as compared with covering A will have to be 12p for every additional £1 in purchase price at a discount rate of 5%, but would have to increase to 16p for every additional £1 of purchase price at a discount rate of 10%.

4.27 It is beyond the scope of this book to enter into an extensive discussion of the principles upon which the choice of discount rate is based. In the best of all possible worlds the discount rate should be the opportunity cost of capital: the real rate of return available on the best alternative use of the funds to be devoted to the proposed project. A moment's thought will indicate, however, that the 'best alternative use' is not easy, and often impossible to identify. In these circumstances the real (net of inflation) long-term cost of borrowing money in the market place – the real rate at which the owner would expect to raise the finance necessary for the project – should be chosen as the discount rate.

4.28 It must be emphasised that the appropriate cost of capital is a long-term cost, where the time period refers to the expected life of the project. Life cycle cost calculations are applied to long-term investment decisions and cannot be expected to be financed by borrowing in short term money markets.

4.29 Even after it has been decided to use the cost of capital as the discount rate, the appropriate rate will vary with the source of funding. There are three important categories of finance available to companies, which, ranked in descending order of their probable costs are as follows.

- Funds from the issue of shares.

- Retained earnings.

- All flows of fixed interest debt capital.

4.30 Since new issues are likely to constitute the most expensive form of funding, and fixed interest capital the least expensive, a company might be expected always to choose fixed interest capital. However, lenders will generally restrict the amount of long term debt capital that can be raised by the company since this constitutes a prior charge on the company. Similarly, there will be restrictions on the proportion of earnings that a company can retain, if only from the need to maintain a reasonable return to equity holders in the company.

4.31 Where the company is forced to adopt a form of funding other than fixed interest capital, problems may arise in identifying the cost of borrowing. If the project is financed from retained earnings, the required rate of return will be less than that required on new issues since the company can obtain the return required by equity holders from a lower return on retained earnings. This arises because finance provided by retained earnings offers substantial tax savings; specifically, the company need not take into account the tax liability incurred by equity holders on dividend payments. Thus the appropriate rate of discount if funding is solely by retained earnings should be the cost of equity finance adjusted appropriately for tax savings.

4.32 Further problems arise where the project is funded by a mix of some or all of the three sources of finance identified above. Two main mixes should be considered.

● *Retained earnings and fixed interest capital.*
In this case the appropriate discount rate will be a weighted average of the returns required on these two types of capital. The weights appropriate to calculating this average are the proportions in which the two types of capital will be used to finance the project. Thus, if a company plans to finance a new building by a mixture of 80% retained earnings and 20% debt capital, and if the required returns on these two sources of finance are 11.5% and 4% respectively, the weighted cost of capital would be:

$$(0.8 \times 11.5) + (0.2 \times 4.0) = 10.0\%$$

● *New issues and fixed interest capital.*
Assuming that a company has raised the maximum feasible loans on its existing assets and income, further loans can be raised only when an appropriate proportion of new equity finance is provided. The cost of finance in this case will be a weighted average of the returns required on equity and debt capital. Assuming proportions of 80% equity and 20% new debt and required returns of 14.0% and 4.0% respectively, the weighted cost of capital would be:

$$(0.8 \times 14.0) + (0.2 \times 4.0) = 12.0\%$$

4.33 It should be noted that if the project is financed by a mix of retained earnings and new equity capital, the cost of capital should be the cost of the equity capital. The company will, presumably, consider this option only when it is already retaining something approaching the maximum practical proportion of earnings. New issues will not alleviate this position; indeed, a new issue may reduce the proportion of earnings that the company feels able to retain. In this case, therefore, the lower return required on retained earnings is irrelevant, since if the project under consideration proves to be unacceptable, the reduction in capital requirements will be made in the relatively expensive new share issue source of funds. In other words, the marginal cost of capital in this case is the cost of externally raised equity capital, and this is the standard against which the project should be measured.

III: Project life

4.34 The third major component of discounting is an estimate of the probable life of the project. Many factors will influence this estimate, and these do not allow the formulation of hard and fast rules. Wherever possible, estimates of probable material and component lives should be obtained from specialist suppliers. In many cases, however, the surveyor will be forced to rely upon historical data and professional judgement.

4.35 The effects of variation in project life are considered below. It is sufficient to state at this stage that the shorter the project life, the more important it is that the estimate of project life be accurate.

Choosing between alternative options

I: Ranking projects with identical lives

4.36 One of the major purposes of discounting techniques within the context of life cycle cost is to allow the decision-taker to choose between possible methods of achieving a given objective. Thus a choice may have to be made between different plan shapes, building aspects, lighting options, glazing options, or floor coverings in situations where the options are mutually exclusive: it is not possible to put a 5-storey and 10-storey building of equal floor space on the same piece of land. The decision-taker must, therefore, be able to use discounting methods to rank the options which are presented.

4.37 The method of ranking depends upon how the calculations are presented. Two basic approaches are available if the options being ranked have identical forecast lives; the absolute and incremental approaches. With the absolute approach the NPV for each possibility is evaluated prior to comparison. The incremental approach, on the other hand, takes one option as the base – it does not matter which – and calculates the NPV of the difference between that base and any other. Both methods will give the same ranking provided all options have the same forecast lives.

4.38 An example may make this clearer.

Example 4

A client can choose between three methods of floor covering for a new office building. All coverings are assumed to have the same lives, forecast as 5 years, after which they will need to be replaced. They have no resale value. The cost of capital adjusted for inflation is 5%, and installation and running costs at current prices are detailed in table 4.D. Capital allowances, at 100%, are taken fully in the first year, and Corporation Tax is assumed to be payable at 50%.

Table 4D: Costs: example 4

Costs		Floor covering option					
		A		B		C	
		Gross	Net of tax	Gross	Net of tax	Gross	Net of tax
Installation		10,000	5000	11,200	5600	13,600	6800
Running costs in year	1	1000	500	600	300	400	200
	2	1000	500	700	350	400	200
	3	1400	700	1100	550	600	300
	4	1800	900	1500	750	800	400
	5	2400	1200	2000	1000	1200	600

Which option should the client choose?

(i.) Absolute approach:
Calculations are presented in table 4.E.

Table 4E: Present value: absolute approach: example 4

Year	Present value factor @ 5%	Present value of costs* for option		
		A	B	C
0	1.000	5000.00	5600.00	6800.00
1	0.952	476.00	285.60	190.40
2	0.907	453.50	317.45	181.40
3	0.864	604.80	475.20	259.20
4	0.823	740.70	617.25	329.20
5	0.784	940.80	784.00	470.40
Total present value		8215.80	**8079.50**	8230.60

* Net of tax.

(ii.) Incremental approach:

Taking option A as the base, net of tax cash flows may be calculated for 'A-B' and 'A-C', and NPV calculated for the hypothetical projects 'A-B' and 'A-C', as in table 4.F.

Table 4F: Present value – incremental approach: Example 4

Year	Present value factor @ 5%	Cash flows*		Present value for	
		A-B	A-C	A-B	A-C
0	1.000	−600	−1800	−600.00	−1800.00
1	0.952	200	300	190.40	285.60
2	0.907	150	300	136.05	272.10
3	0.864	150	400	129.60	345.60
4	0.823	150	500	123.45	411.50
5	0.784	200	600	156.80	470.40
Total present value				**136.30**	**− 14.80**

* Net of tax.

Both methods rank the alternatives in the order: B, A, C.

4.39 It may be noted that with the absolute approach the best, that is lowest cost, option is that with the lowest present value, whereas with the incremental approach, the best option is that with the highest net present value. The apparent difference in ranking procedure arises since in life cycle cost, cash flows will typically be costs rather than revenues. In terms of equations (4.II) and (4.III) above, costs will enter the calculations as negative numbers.

4.40 It is more convenient in these circumstances to ignore the negative signs and choose that option with the lowest present value, since this is equivalent to the lowest cost.

4.41 When using the incremental approach, on the other hand, the hypothetical project 'A-B', for example, incurs costs of installation, but then offers savings (revenues) on running costs. The best option is that with the highest positive NPV: note that the hypothetical project 'A-A' has an NPV of zero. Thus option B offers additional savings with a net present value of £136.30 when compared with option A, while option C incurs additional cost with a net present value of £14.80.

4.42 The incremental approach offers no advantages when compared with the absolute approach, since both use exactly the same information. It does, however, present problems when options have different projected lives, since it will be necessary to create hypothetical projects with identical lives before comparison is possible. In addition, it will often be the case that life cycle cost techniques will be applied in cases where 'maintain existing system' is one feasible option, for example, when deciding whether to replace a particular building system. It is preferable that costs of the existing system be presented explicitly, rather than that costs for proposed options be presented as changes to existing costs. This will force the surveyor to detail the assumptions made, and will provide the decision-taker with better information.

4.43 For both reasons, it is recommended that the absolute approach be used in life cycle cost calculations. One point should then be emphasised. Any resale value for a particular option should enter as a negative number since it is a deduction from costs. Similarly, if, when a new option such as a new heating system is adopted, the existing system has a resale value, this should also enter as a negative number in the calculations for the proposed new system.

II: Ranking projects with different lives

4.44 The problem remains of the choice between options with different project lives. How, for example, should a building occupier choose between two types of floor covering, one with an estimated life of three years, and the other with an estimated life of five years? One possibility would be to treat the former as five consecutive three-year decisions, and the latter as three consecutive five year decisions, both totalling fifteen years. If, however, there is a third option with an economic life of seven years, it would be necessary to expand the time horizon to 105 years!

4.45 A much simpler procedure is available. The surveyor need only calculate the present value of each possibility and express this as a uniform annuity or annual equivalent (*AE*). The least cost option is that with the lowest *AE*.

In other words, if a particular option has present value of costs equal to *PV*, and expected life of *N* years, we wish to find the *N* year uniform annuity or annual equivalent (*AE*) which has present value of costs equal to *PV*. This annual equivalent is identified from the equation:

$$PV = \sum_{t=1}^{N} \frac{AE}{(1+r)^t} = AE \frac{(1+r)^N - 1}{(1+r)^N \cdot r} \qquad (4.\text{IV})$$

from which follows that:

$$AE = PV \frac{(1+r)^N \cdot r}{(1+r)^N - 1} \qquad (4.\text{V})$$

4.46 For example, a project may be considered with an economic life of 10 years, and *PV* of costs of £5,000 at a discount rate of 5%. Using equation (4.V):

$$AE = £5000 \cdot \frac{(1.05)^{10} \times 0.05}{(1.05)^{10} - 1} = £647.50$$

4.47 Thus, the present value of the cost stream (£5,000) is equivalent to a uniform cost stream of £647.50 over the 10 year life of the project at a discount rate of 5%.

4.48 Calculation of *AE* is considerably simplified by using annuity tables. An annuity of £1 per annum for ten years at 5% has present value:

$$PVA = £7.722$$

and comparing equations (4.IV) and (4.V) it follows that:

$$AE = \frac{PV}{PVA} = \frac{£5000}{7.722} = £647.50 \qquad (4.\text{VI})$$

4.49 An example may further clarify this principle.

Example 5

In the case of the floor covering options of example 4, it may now be considered that option B has a project life of 6 years and option C a project life of 8 years. The inflation adjusted discount rate is 5%. Tax rates are as in example 4, and net of tax costs for option A are as in table 4.D while those for options B and C are as in table 4.G.

Now option C should be chosen as the lowest cost alternative.

4.50 This example should also serve to emphasise why the incremental approach should not be adopted when alternative options have different forecast lives. The incremental approach cannot be applied directly to the data in table 4.G since there is no information on the costs of option A, for example, in years 6, 7 and 8. Converting these options to equivalent lives, on the other hand, requires analysis of the projects over a minimum period of 120 years.

Internal rate of return (IRR)

4.51 While the discussion in previous sections has concentrated on discounted cash

Table 4G: Present value calculations: example 5

Year	Costs* for option			Present value factor @ 5%	Present value of costs		
	A	B	C		A	B	C
0	5000	5600	6800	1.000	5000.00	5600.00	6800.00
1	500	300	200	0.952	476.00	285.60	190.40
2	500	350	200	0.907	453.50	317.45	181.40
3	700	550	300	0.864	604.80	475.20	259.20
4	900	750	400	0.823	740.70	617.25	329.20
5	1200	1000	600	0.784	940.80	784.00	470.40
6		1200	800	0.746		895.20	596.80
7			1000	0.711			711.00
8			1200	0.677			812.40
Total present value (PV)					8215.80	8974.70	10350.80
Present value of annuity (PVA)					4.329	5.076	6.463
Annual equivalent (AE = PV/PVA)					1897.85	1768.07	1601.55

* Net of tax.

flow and net present value, some comments are necessary on an alternative method of investment appraisal – the internal rate of return (IRR).

4.52 The IRR for a project is defined as that discount rate which generates an NPV of zero. Recalling equation (4.II):

$$NPV = \sum_{t=0}^{N} \frac{R_t - C_t}{(1 + r)^t}$$

while IRR is that interest rate k which is such that:

$$NPV_k = \sum_{t=0}^{N} \frac{R_t - C_t}{(1 + k)^t} = 0 \qquad (4.VII)$$

4.53 The first limitation of IRR as a method of ranking for life cycle cost purposes is that it can be applied only if the incremental approach is adopted: if all cash flows on an option are negative (that is, are costs), no IRR can be calculated.

4.54 Many more serious criticisms can be levelled at IRR in comparison with NPV as a method of ranking alternatives. IRR is more difficult to calculate, can give inconsistent recommendations, and contains logical error in its methodology. To detail these criticisms is beyond the scope of this book. The interested reader can check them in any text on capital investment appraisal.[1] Suffice it to say that there are compelling reasons for preferring present value comparison as the method of appraisal for life cycle cost purposes.

Inflation

4.55 It must be accepted that inflation in particular costs is important. Indeed, it can be argued that one of the main reasons for the growing interest in life cycle cost has been precisely because certain costs, such as energy and labour, have risen sharply in recent years and called into question the traditional design approach. It is also unlikely that we shall ever return to a regime of stable prices. As a consequence, present value calculations within a life cycle cost framework must be capable of taking inflation into account. Methods for doing so will now be considered in detail.

4.56 The simplest method might appear to be to evaluate all cash flows in real terms and discount at an inflation-free discount rate. Thus, if a project is expected to generate costs of £1,000 per annum for 5 years, evaluated at today's prices, if all

[1] See, for example, Levy, H & Sarnat, M (1982): *Capital Investment and Financial Decisions* (2nd edition), Prentice Hall International, esp. chapter 4.

costs are expected to rise at 10% per annum over the five years, and if the market cost of capital is 15.5%, the simplest approach will be to discount the cost stream at 5%.

4.57 It must be accepted that in many instances this will be the best information available at the time of analysis. Indeed, it will often be the case that when the surveyor prepares a life cycle cost plan there may not even be an adequate estimate of expected escalation rates. Where this is so, the surveyor should adopt an approach identical to that recommended by Government with respect to investment in the public sector and apply a test discount rate. Just what should this test discount rate be? Recent analysis indicates that when inflation rates are reasonably low (less than 15%) there is quite a stable relationship between inflation and bank base rate, implying a real discount rate of between 4% and 5%. If no better information is available, therefore, it is recommended that a test discount rate of 4% be used.

4.58 It must be emphasised, that the test discount rate should be used only if better information is not available to the surveyor, since it is crucially dependent upon the assumption that inflation will apply equally to all future cash flows on the project. In some cases this may be sufficiently true to be taken as a working approximation, or may be necessary because of lack of information, but in any complex investment project a wide range of different factors – labour, fuel, materials – will be involved, the costs of which can be expected to inflate at different rates.

4.59 In circumstances where different components can be expected to increase in price at different rates and where adequate information on relative inflation rates can be generated, a much more sophisticated approach should be adopted in incorporating inflation into the analysis. Essentially, what this involves is the evaluation of each component in money terms prior to discounting at a cost of capital inclusive of an allowance for inflation, *i.e.* the market generated cost of capital. An example may serve to make this clearer.

Example 6

A firm proposing to build a new office is considering two design options with costs detailed in table 4.H. These costs are assumed to be net of all tax allowances.

Table 4H: Hypothetical office costs: example 6

	Option A	Option B
Construction costs	£1.5m	£2.0m
Running costs (current value)		
(i) Energy (heating, lighting, air conditioning)	£100th	£80th
(ii) Cleaning (labour the only variable)	£40th	£30th
(iii) Maintenance:		
Labour	£30th	£24th
Materials	£10th	£8th
Expected building life	15 years	15 years
Resale value (allowing for inflation)	£3.0m	£3.0m
Cost of capital	15%	
Expected inflation rate		
Energy	11%	
Labour	8%	
Materials	8%	

NB: All cash flows are in current prices with the exception of the resale value.

Which design option should be chosen?

To calculate present values it is first necessary to calculate discount rates for the various costs.

(i) **Energy costs** are expected to inflate at 11% and should be discounted at 15%. This is equivalent to a discount rate of $(1.15/1.11) - 1 = 3.6\%$.

Using 15 year annuity factors:

@ 3% = 11.938

@ 4% = 11.118

hence @ 3.6% = 11.938 × 0.4 + 11.1181 × 0.6 = 11.446

(ii) **Cleaning costs** are expected to inflate at 8%.
The discount rate is $(1.15/1.08) - 1 = 6.5\%$

The 15 year annuity factor @ 6.5% = 9.410

(iii) **Maintenance costs** are expected to inflate at 8%.
The discount rate is $(1.15/1.08) - 1 = 6.5\%$

The 15 year annuity factor @ 6.5% = 9.410

Given these discount rates, present value calculations are as in table 4.J.

Table 4J: Present values (£m): example 6

	Cash flow A	Cash flow B	Annuity factor	Present value factor @ 14%	Present value A	Present value B
Construction	1.5	2.0	–	–	1.5	2.0
Running costs						
Energy	0.1	0.08	11.446	–	1.145	0.916
Cleaning	0.04	0.03	9.410	–	0.376	0.282
Maintenance						
Labour	0.03	0.024	9.410	–	0.282	0.226
Materials	0.01	0.008	9.410	–	0.094	0.075
Resale value	–3.0	–3.0	–	0.140	–0.42	–0.42
Total present value (£m)					2.977	3.079

Option A should be chosen since it is the lower cost option.

4.60   It can be seen from example 6 that so long as the rate of inflation of a particular cost estimate is less than the market discount rate the principles of present value calculation are precisely those already discussed. All that is needed is calculation of the net of inflation discount rate. If expected inflation of a particular cost element is $i\%$, and the market rate of discount is $r\%$, the net of inflation discount rate the surveyor should use is:

$$d = \frac{1+r}{1+i} - 1 \qquad (4.\text{VIII})$$

For instance, in example 6 with $d = 15\%$ and $i = 8\%$ the net of inflation discount rate is:

$$\frac{1.15}{1.08} - 1 = 6.5\%$$

4.61   Complications arise, however, when the expected inflation rate for particular costs exceeds the cost of capital. The method of calculation presented in table 4.J cannot be used for such costs.

4.62   It may be assumed that a particular cost, estimated at today's prices as £C per annum, is expected to inflate at an annual rate of $i\%$ over its life of N years. The discount rate is $r\%$. Then the present value of these costs is:

$$PV = \sum_{t=0}^{N} \frac{C.(1+i)^t}{(1+r)^t} = C \cdot \frac{\left(\frac{1+i}{1+r}\right)^N - 1}{\frac{1+i}{1+r} - 1} \cdot \frac{1+i}{1+r} \qquad (4.\text{IX})$$

4.63   Calculation of the present value in equation (4.IX) is considerably simplified by defining a *net inflation rate* (e) by the formula:

$$1 + e = (1+i) / (1+r)$$

Thus, for example, if expected inflation is 17.3% and market cost of capital is 15%

$$1 + e = 1.173/1.15 = 1.02$$

then the net inflation rate is 2%. It is then possible to tabulate the present value of £1 per annum at various net inflation rates. These values are detailed in appendix A to this chapter.

4.64 The net inflation rate is, in fact, used when the effective (real) discount rate is negative. This can be illustrated by considering a situation in which a client can borrow £1,000 to upgrade his building insulation, so reducing heating and ventilating costs. The client has been advised that heating and ventilating costs are expected to escalate at 15% per annum, while he can borrow the £1,000 at a market rate of 12% per annum. In these circumstances, if the client upgrades the insulation, the future savings achieved will actually be growing at an effective rate of 2.7%, equivalent to a discount rate of –2.6%. To see why this is so, note that with inflation at 15%, a £1 reduction in fuel costs at today's prices is equivalent to £1.15 in one year's time, and at a discount rate of 12% this has a present value of £1.15/1.12 = £1.027: a growth or net inflation rate of 2.7%. Putting this in terms of discount rates, what is needed is that discount rate r which is such that $1/(1 + r) = 1.027$. Solving this equation gives r = –0.026, *i.e.* a discount rate of –2.6%. Appendix A notes the effective (negative) discount rates associated with each net inflation rate. For example, a net inflation rate of 2% is equivalent to a negative discount rate of –1.96%.

4.65 As an illustration of these equations, it may be assumed in example 6 that energy costs are forecast to increase at 17.3% per annum. Then the net inflation rate is given by $1 + e = 1.173/1.15 = 1.02$, that is e is 2%.

From example 6:

C = £100 th. for option A
C = £80 th. for option B

Using equation (4.IX) the forecast value of energy costs is (in £m):

$$\text{Option A: } 0.10 \times \frac{\left(\frac{1.173}{1.15}\right)^{15} - 1}{\frac{1.173}{1.15} - 1} \times \frac{1.173}{1.15} = £1.764 \text{ m}$$

$$\text{Option B: } 0.08 \times \frac{\left(\frac{1.173}{1.15}\right)^{15} - 1}{\frac{1.173}{1.15} - 1} \times \frac{1.173}{1.15} = £1.411 \text{ m}$$

4.66 Alternatively, consulting appendix A with net inflation rate 2% and project life 15 years, the present value of an inflating annuity is 17.639, and the same results are obtained. Note that in these circumstances option B in example 6 would be the preferred option.

4.67 As a general rule, it is to be expected that once inflation is allowed for in the analysis, investment decisions will become much more sensitive to future operating costs. Inflation reduces the effective discount rate. The greater is the expected rate of inflation relative to the money cost of capital, the greater will be the consequent reduction in the effective discount rate.

Risk, uncertainty and sensitivity analysis

4.68 The concluding remarks in paragraph 4.67 hint at one relatively important feature of life cycle cost calculations. The majority of such calculations will be based upon assumptions about the costs of fuel, cleaning, maintenance and so on consequent upon a design decision with an estimated initial capital cost. Forecasts will be made regarding future escalation rates of these various costs, and an estimate will be made of the probable project life.

4.69 Clearly, the cash flows, escalation rates and project life cannot be known with certainty. Rather, information will be available only on the likely bounds within which they will lie, or the range of possibilities.

4.70 There is now an extensive literature on [...] under uncertainty. All that needs to be emphasize[d...] [sho]uld be based upon the best possible information. I[t...] [th]is is an area in which the surveyor is uniquely qua[lified...] the surveyor's expertise lies in the production of [...ba]sic data that are inevitably uncertain.

4.71 It should also be noted that simpl[...] facilitate identification of the most important, or sens[itive...] particular, once estimates have been made it is recommended [...] s of the life cycle cost calculations be subjected to a sensitivity analysis (s[ee p.] 4.21) with respect to those estimates or assumptions felt to be most uncertain.

4.72 Sensitivity analysis is a technique that analyses the effects on a project's viability of variations in particular elements of that project. The technique is best illustrated by means of an example.

Example 7

A client has to choose between two glazing options, each with uncertain economic life. Costs of these options are detailed in table 4.K. All figures are adjusted for taxation and there is assumed to be no inflation. The client expects the cost of capital to be between 5% and 8%.

Table 4K: Cost data: example 7

Costs*	Option A (£th)	Option B (£th)
Installation costs	150	100
Annual costs of energy loss	15-25	25-35
Additional annual cleaning and operating costs	10-15	15-20

* Net of tax.

Calculation of the present value of these options will result in a complex of results since there is no direct knowledge of either project life or the actual cost of capital. Four basic cases can, however, be identified for each option as in table 4.L and the present values for these cases can be illustrated in the graphical form of *figure 4.3*.

4.73 The graphical analysis of *figure 4.3* allows immediate identification of the variables that have important effects on the choice. It focuses attention on the critical outcomes, and makes the possible range of estimates clear. The final decision resulting from the sensitivity analysis remains a matter of subjective judgement, of course, but the decision-taker now has much more solid information on which to base that judgement, and can identify the effects of his decision much more clearly.

4.74 This point must be emphasised. No definitive rules can be laid down for decision making in uncertain conditions. Such decisions will inevitably be based on value judgements and, in particular, on the attitude of the individual decision maker. This section has shown, however, that correct presentation of data will be of significant benefit to those who carry the responsibility for the final decision.

Table 4L: Possible cash flows for example 7 (£th)

	Option A			Option B		
	Energy costs	Operating costs	Total annual costs	Energy costs	Operating costs	Total annual costs
Case 1	15	10	25	25	15	40
Case 2	15	15	30	25	20	45
Case 3	25	10	35	35	15	50
Case 4	25	15	40	35	20	55

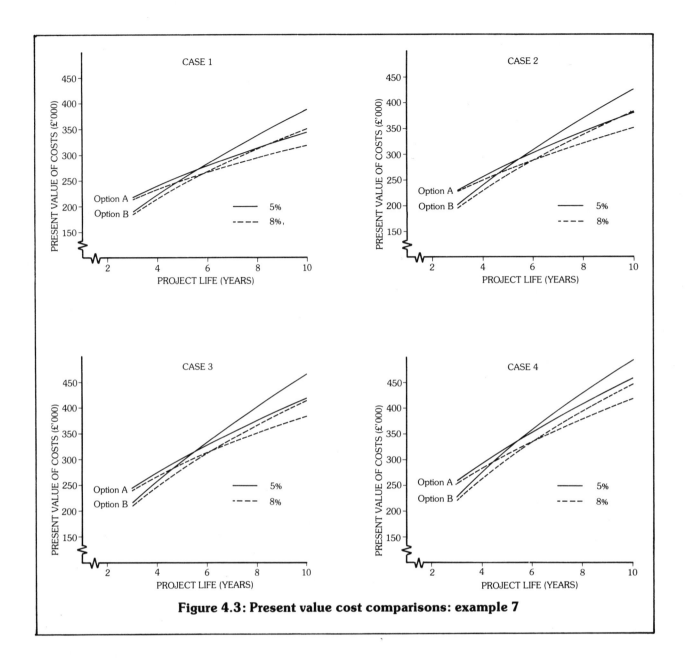

Figure 4.3: Present value cost comparisons: example 7

Conclusions

4.75 The major aim of this chapter has been to indicate how particular investment appraisal techniques can be applied to life cycle cost. These techniques are necessary, firstly, because money today and money tomorrow are not equivalent and secondly, because life cycle cost is applicable precisely in those conditions where costs are arising over time.

4.76 It has been shown that while there are several methods of investment appraisal, only one is properly applicable to life cycle costs. Projects should be assessed on the basis of their present values, using a discount rate equal to the real long term cost of capital to the organisation. Methods such as pay-back period and internal rate of return are not appropriate for life cycle cost purposes.

4.77 Complications will arise if the options being compared have different economic lives, or are subject to inflation, or involve estimates that are uncertain.

4.78 Techniques have been presented to allow the surveyor to incorporate differences in project lives or inflation in the analysis. Problems remain, however, with respect to uncertainty. In these circumstances a sensitivity analysis should be performed. This will identify those assumptions or estimates to which the viability of the project is most sensitive. It will, therefore, improve the information base upon which the decision-taker will make the eventual choice.

Chapter 4: Appendix A

Present value rate of £1 at net inflation rate

Number of Years	1%	2%	3%	4%	5%	6%	7%	8%	9%	10%
1	1.009	1.020	1.030	1.040	1.050	1.060	1.070	1.080	1.090	1.100
2	2.030	2.060	2.091	2.122	2.153	2.184	2,215	2.246	2.278	2.310
3	3.060	3.122	3.184	3.246	3.310	3.375	3.440	3.506	3.573	3.641
4	4.101	4.204	4.309	4.416	4.526	4.637	4.751	4.867	4.985	5.105
5	5.152	5.308	5.468	5.633	5.802	5.975	6.153	6.336	6.523	6.716
6	6.214	6.434	6.662	6.898	7.142	7.394	7.654	7.923	8.200	8.487
7	7.286	7.583	7.892	8.214	8.549	8.897	9.260	9.637	10.020	10.436
8	8.369	8.755	9.159	9.583	10.027	10.492	10.978	11.488	12.021	12.579
9	9.462	9.950	10.464	11.006	11.578	12.181	12.816	13.487	14.193	14.937
10	10.567	11.169	11.808	12.486	13.207	13.972	14.784	15.645	16.560	17.531
11	11.683	12.412	13.192	14.026	14.917	15.870	16.888	17.977	19.141	20.384
12	12.809	13.680	14.618	15.627	16.713	17.882	19.141	20.495	21.953	23.523
13	13.947	14.974	16.086	17.292	18.599	20.015	21.550	23.215	25.019	26.975
14	15.097	16.292	17.599	19.024	20.579	22.276	24.129	26.152	28.361	30.772
15	16.258	17.639	19.157	20.825	22.657	24.673	26.888	29.324	32.003	34.950
16	17.430	19.012	20.762	22.698	24.840	27.213	29.840	32.750	35.974	39.545
17	18.615	20.412	22.414	24.645	27.132	29.906	32.999	36.450	40.301	44.599
18	19.811	21.841	24.117	26.671	29.539	32.760	36.379	40.446	45.018	50.159
19	20.019	23.297	25.870	28.778	32.066	35.786	39.995	44.762	50.160	56.275
20	22.239	24.783	27.676	30.969	34.719	38.993	43.865	49.423	55.765	63.003
21	23.472	26.299	29.537	33.248	37.505	42.392	48.006	54.457	61.873	70.403
22	24.716	27.845	31.453	35.618	40.430	45.996	52.436	59.893	68.532	78.543
23	25.973	29.422	33.426	38.083	43.502	49.816	57.177	65.765	75.790	87.497
24	27.243	31.030	35.459	40.646	46.727	53.865	62.249	72.106	83.701	97.347
25	28.526	32.671	37.553	43.312	50.113	58.156	67.676	78.954	92.324	108.182
26	29.821	34.344	39.710	46.084	53.669	62.706	73.485	86.351	101.723	120.100
27	31.129	36.051	41.931	48.986	57.403	67.528	79.698	94.339	111.968	133.210
28	32.450	37.792	44.219	51.966	61.323	72.640	86.347	102.966	123.135	147.631
29	33.785	39.568	46.575	55.085	65.439	78.058	93.461	112.283	135.308	163.494
30	35.133	41.379	49.003	58.328	69.761	83.803	101.073	122.346	148.575	180.943
31	36.494	43.227	51.503	61.701	74.299	89.890	109.218	133.214	163.037	200.138
32	37.869	45.112	54.078	65.210	79.064	96.343	117.933	144.951	178.800	221.252
33	39.258	47.034	56.730	68.858	84.067	103.184	127.259	157.627	195.982	244.477
34	40.660	48.994	59.462	72.652	89.320	110.435	137.237	171.317	214.711	270.024
35	42.077	50.994	62.276	76.598	94.836	118.121	147.913	186.102	235.125	298.127
36	43.508	53.034	65.174	80.702	100.628	126.268	159.337	202.070	257.376	329.039
37	44.953	55.115	68.159	84.970	106.710	134.904	171.561	219.316	281.630	363.043
38	46.412	57.237	71.234	89.409	113.095	144.058	184.640	237.941	308.066	400.448
39	47.886	59.402	74.401	94.026	119.800	153.762	198.635	258.057	336.882	441.593
40	49.375	61.610	77.663	98.827	126.840	164.048	213.610	279.781	368.292	486.852
Effective (negative) discount rate (%)	−0.99	−1.96	−2.91	−3.85	−4.76	−5.66	−6.54	−7.41	−8.26	−9.09

Chapter 4: Appendix B

Summary of discounting equations

1. Present value of £X received in time t at discount rate $r\%$:

   $$\text{PV of X} = X/(1 + r)^t$$

2. Present value factor:

   $$\text{PVF} = 1/(1 + r)^t$$

3. Present value of costs C_t at discount rate $r\%$ and project life N years:

   $$\text{PV} = \sum_{t=0}^{N} \frac{C_t}{(1 + r)^t}$$

4. Present value of an annuity of £1 for N years at discount rate $r\%$:

   $$\text{PVA} = \frac{(1 + r)^N - 1}{(1 + r)^N \cdot r}$$

5. Annual equivalent of present value (PV) over N years at discount rate $r\%$:

   $$\text{UA} = \text{PV} \cdot \frac{(1 + r)^N \cdot r}{((1 + r)^N - 1)} = \frac{\text{PV}}{\text{PVA}}$$

6. Present value of a current cost £C with inflation rate $i\%$ and nominal discount rate $r\%$:

   $$\text{PV} = C \cdot \frac{\left(\frac{1 + i}{1 + d}\right)^N - 1}{\frac{1 + i}{1 + d} - 1} \cdot \frac{1 - i}{1 - d}$$

7. Discount rate applied to a cost escalating at $i\%$, with nominal discount rate $d\%$ (d greater than i):

   $$r = \frac{1 + d}{1 + i} - 1$$

8. Net inflation rate for a cost inflating at $i\%$, with nominal discount rate $d\%$ (d less than i):

   $$e = \frac{1 + i}{1 + d} - 1$$

Chapter 5

Key Points

- Any system can provide results that are only as good as the original data will allow (para. 5.2).

- There are three important data sources: specialist manufacturers, suppliers, and contractors; modelling techniques; and historical data (para. 5.4).

- Specialist manufacturers and suppliers can be expected to have detailed knowledge of the performance characteristics of their products (para. 5.5).

- Specialist contractors can advise on and provide information on the running cost implications of design decisions, *e.g.* cleaning (para. 5.6).

- Models reduce complex systems to their essential component parts (para. 5.8).

- Experience will improve data obtained both from specialist suppliers and contractors and from model building techniques (paras. 5.7 and 5.11).

- Effective life cycle costing requires identification of those areas in which running costs are most sensitive to changes in design decisions (para. 5.15).

- It is to be expected that both initial and capital cost will differ quite significantly with building type (para. 5.16).

- Just as the quantity surveyor uses only 'comparable' buildings as a source of historical cost data when estimating initial capital costs, so similar selection criteria should be made when estimating running costs (para. 5.21).

- Data should be selected for analysis in a structured way (para. 5.28). Criteria such as age, occupancy, function, type of construction, should be used as selection criteria (para. 5.31).

- Existing sources of historical data are imperfect but will improve with experience and use (para. 5.32).

- The running costs of buildings will vary with building type and with building design. Rarely will two very similar buildings have identical running costs (para. 5.36).

5

Data sources for life cycle cost purposes

The importance of improving data accuracy

5.1 There are three fundamental requirements in the implementation of life cycle costing.

- A system by which the techniques can be used: a set of rules and procedures.

- Data for the proposed project under consideration: estimates of initial and running costs, of life cycle(s), discount rates, inflation indices, periods of occupancy, energy consumption, cleaning, and so on.

- Professional skill and judgement.

5.2 While the system by which data are analysed is crucially important, it must be emphasised that any such system can provide results that are only as good as the original data will allow. If the basic data are inaccurate, then no amount of modelling or sophisticated analysis will give results that are anything other than inaccurate. Effective decision-making based on life cycle cost calculations is possible only if the data input to the analytical process is sufficiently reliable to impose reasonable limits on the uncertainty inevitably associated with all fore-casting. It follows that there are significant benefits to be gained, in both the accuracy and value of results, from efforts aimed at improving the quality of the basic information and data to which life cycle cost techniques are applied.

5.3 Data used in life cycle costing may be physical, performance, qualitative, or cost data (see chapter 3). Life cycle costing has cost as its purpose, hence this chapter considers possible sources of cost data available to quantity surveyors. The most important of these data sources – historical data – is examined in some detail.

Basic data sources

5.4 Data for life cycle cost purposes are available from three main sources: specialist manufacturers, suppliers and contractors; modelling techniques; historical data.

I: Data from specialist manufacturers, suppliers and contractors

5.5 The majority of building components are bought from specialist manufacturers and suppliers, the construction process being mainly a complex assembly operation on site. Specialist manufacturers and suppliers can be expected to have detailed knowledge of the performance characteristics of their materials and components, but this knowledge will have been influenced by the ways in which buildings are used. Nevertheless, the extensive knowledge and experience of specialist manufacturers and suppliers are a valuable source of life cycle cost information. Wherever possible, manufacturers and suppliers should be asked to provide details of the performance characteristics of the products they are sup-plying, related to such aspects as expected operating life, maintenance require-ments, energy use, cleaning requirements, etc.

5.6 Specialist contractors should also be consulted. For example, specialist cleaning contractors are able to provide information at the design stage on the cleaning cost implications of particular design decisions and choices of materials. Furth-ermore, the heavy concentration on repair and maintenance in the U.K. building industry is such that extensive expertise is now available on maintenance requirements and failure characteristics of different building components.

5.7 It might be argued that the data provided by specialists will be little more than 'best guesses'. To an extent this may be true but the effects of experience and learning should not be underrated. With experience, suppliers, manufacturers and contractors can be expected to develop a closer understanding of the building elements with which they are dealing. As more clients demand this type of information, and subsequently check the information against performance, substantial improvements in accuracy and reliability should ensue.

II: Data from model building

5.8 The essence of a model is to reduce a complex system to its essential component parts. Models can be very complex. In weather forecasting, for example, models are used to represent complete meteorological systems. In economic forecasting, the Treasury model of the U.K. economy consists of more than 500 equations. Nevertheless, these models only approximate reality – a full representation of the U.K. economy would require almost a full set of equations for every person in the economy. The crucial property of a 'good' model is that it captures the fundamental properties of complicated systems without having to resort to complete representation of those systems.

5.9 So it is with models applied to buildings. Particular features of buildings lend themselves to modelling. The models can then be used to analyse the life cycle cost implications of particular design decisions or choices of materials. As an example, the majority of cleaning costs in an office building will be incurred in cleaning walls, floors and windows. A simple model could be constructed as follows.

(i) Identify type, location and superficial area of different types of surface finishes: such as tiles, carpets, paintwork, glass, etc.

(ii) Draw up a flow diagram using the information in (i).

(iii) Estimate labour, material, plant and overhead requirements and costs per unit area of materials to be cleaned, making due allowance for wastage of materials and the sequence of work. These requirements will, of course, vary with the frequency of cleaning and standard of cleaning required.

(iv) Apply the unit costs in (iii) to the areas in (i) using the flow diagram in (ii) to give an overall cost for cleaning related to a cleaning programme.

5.10 Clearly much more complicated models can be constructed, but are beyond the scope of this book. What should be clear, however, is that model building is important in life cycle costing. It can be used, in particular, where historical data are either not available, or are available in too aggregate a form to be applicable and usable, or where the model builder, in this case the surveyor producing a life cycle cost plan, has a better overview of the building as a system than any other specialist.

5.11 Model building should not be seen as independent of the other forms of cost estimation: even the simple model structure outlined above requires cost estimates as input at some stage in the modelling process.

However, the more experience that quantity surveyors gain with modelling the systems for which they are producing estimates, the better they will be able to identify the important components of those systems.

III: Historical data: relative cost impact of selected cost items

5.12 Historical data sources will produce profiles of initial costs and running costs which are likely to be very different. If an elemental breakdown of initial building costs and a similar breakdown of running costs are analysed into the same categories for a proposed building and compared, an indication will be obtained of those areas in which a life cycle cost approach is likely to prove most effective in reducing the total building costs. If a particular building element, *e.g.* foundations, takes a relatively high proportion of initial costs, but has very low subsequent running costs, little is to be gained from the application of life cycle cost techniques to this element. On the other hand, significant running costs may be indicative of potential life cycle cost savings through a change in design decisions. It is then necessary to investigate the sensitivity of the running costs to changes in design or operating procedures.

5.13 *Figure 5.1* illustrates such comparative cost data for an office building. The initial costs are the construction costs. All the running cost data have been discounted to a net present value over a life of 30 years at a discount rate of 5%. Energy costs include all energy-consuming elements of a building, *i.e.* heating, cooling, ventilation, air conditioning, lighting, hot water and other miscellaneous loads. Maintenance costs include the costs of regular inspection and repair, annual maintenance contracts, and salaries of staff performing maintenance tasks. Replacement of items of less than £2,500 in value or having a life of less than 5

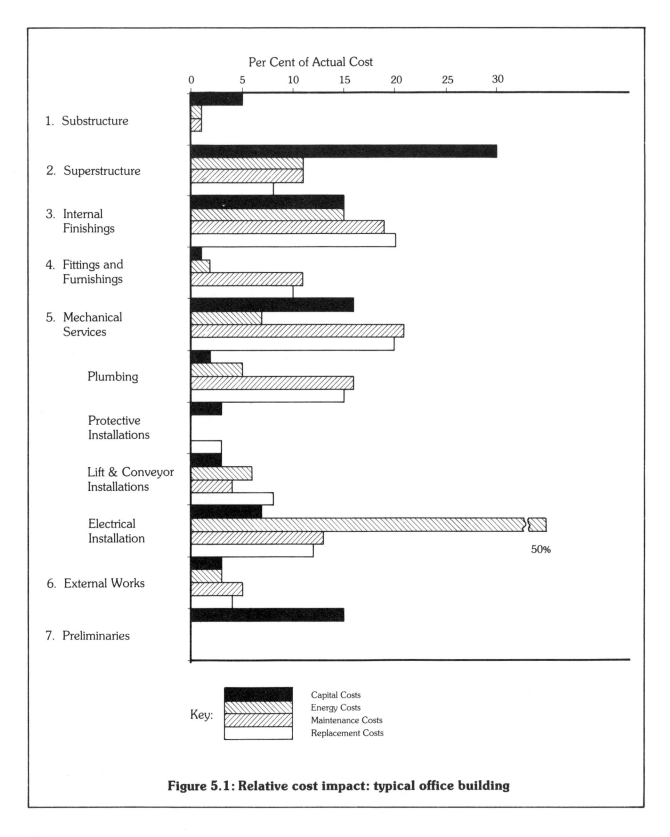

Figure 5.1: Relative cost impact: typical office building

years are included as part of maintenance. Building replacement costs include the cost of replacing the many equipment or other elements with an estimated life cycle shorter than that planned for the entire building.

5.14   As can be seen, there are some quite marked differences in the cost breakdowns of these four cost areas. Substructure and superstructure contribute a significant proportion (35%) of initial costs, but account for less than 12% of subsequent energy, maintenance and replacement costs. In contrast, internal finishings and mechanical and electrical services account for a much higher proportion of running costs than of initial capital costs.

5.15   The clear implication of *figure 5.1* is that the benefits of a life cycle cost approach are not likely to be evenly spread throughout all elements of a building. In the first instance at least, attention should be focused on elements such as services and general finishes in the building. It is these elements whose running costs are likely to prove most sensitive to changes in design decisions. As the application of life cycle cost techniques is reasonably complicated and time consuming, such effort should be concentrated on the most fruitful areas of a building.

Running costs of different types of buildings

5.16   The cost analyses discussed in paragraphs 5.13 to 5.15 relate solely to an office building and give no indication of the variances of the various averages presented in *figure 5.1*. It is to be expected that both initial and running costs will differ quite significantly with building type, and that these costs will exhibit quite high degrees of variability.

5.17   Consider the first of these factors – differences in running costs by building type. The main source of such data comes, inevitably, from the U.S.A. where there is greater experience of the application of life cycle cost techniques.

5.18   It is, of course, true that U.S. data cannot be directly transferred to the U.K. environment when making absolute cost comparisons. On the other hand, it is legitimate to use U.S. data to gain an appreciation of variability in costs.

5.19   *Figure 5.2* presents summary statistics of the estimated energy performance of buildings throughout the U.S.A. on which construction began in 1975 or 1976. They are drawn from a sample of 1661 non-residential and 4593 residential data collection forms.

As can be seen, there is very wide variability around the estimated averages, reflecting the impact of variations in both climate and in building design. The U.K. does not exhibit the same climatic variation as the U.S.A. This will mainly affect the range of energy usage by building type, unless there are sharp differences in the spatial distribution of the various building types. It must again be stressed that different types of building generate very different running cost profiles.

5.20   The BMCIS publish occupancy cost analyses for buildings broken down into occupancy categories, *e.g.* decoration, cleaning. it should be noted that the sample sizes are quite small for certain building types, so reducing the confidence that can be placed in the estimates. Table 5.A summarises the data from a study of average running costs.

5.21   The wide difference in average running costs is worthy of note. Just as the quantity surveyor will use only 'comparable' buildings as a source of historical cost data when preparing an estimate of the initial capital costs of a proposed building, so it is clear that similar selection criteria should be used when selecting data suitable for use in estimating running costs.

5.22   In addition, while energy costs are especially important for all building types, other cost areas, in particular cleaning, rates and maintenance are also important and on occasions account for a greater proportion of total running costs.

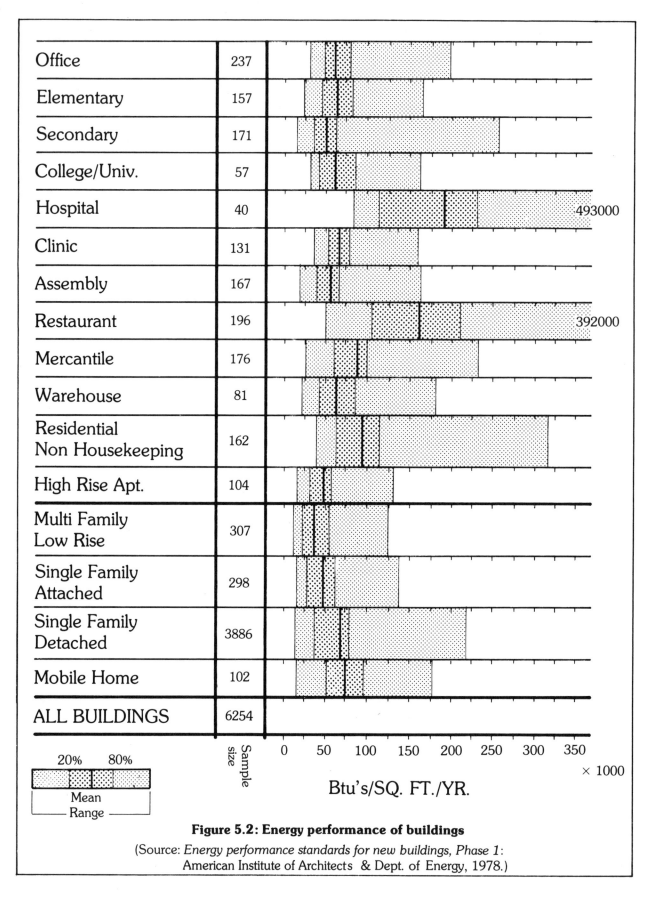

	Sample size								
Office	237								
Elementary	157								
Secondary	171								
College/Univ.	57								
Hospital	40							493000	
Clinic	131								
Assembly	167								
Restaurant	196							392000	
Mercantile	176								
Warehouse	81								
Residential Non Housekeeping	162								
High Rise Apt.	104								
Multi Family Low Rise	307								
Single Family Attached	298								
Single Family Detached	3886								
Mobile Home	102								
ALL BUILDINGS	6254								

20%   80%

Mean
Range

0   50   100   150   200   250   300   350

× 1000

Btu's/SQ. FT./YR.

Figure 5.2: Energy performance of buildings

(Source: *Energy performance standards for new buildings, Phase 1*:
American Institute of Architects & Dept. of Energy, 1978.)

5.23   Inflation in running costs has been significant in recent years. BMCIS published
cost indices, shown in *figure 5.3*, indicate that these costs have more than
doubled over the 5 year period 1974-79, representing an annual rate of inflation
of something in excess of 15%. This implies a real discount rate of some 4-5%
assuming a 20% nominal interest rate (see chapter 4). Applying a 5% discount
rate and 25 year life cycle gives the present value of average running costs,
assuming that they continue to escalate in the same way relative to the nominal
interest rate. As can be seen from table 5.A the range is very wide and gives

Table 5A: BMCIS Study of average running costs (1980)

Building type	Sample Size*	Average running costs (£/£100m²)								Present worth @ (£/m²)§
		Decoration	Fabric	Services	Cleaning	Utilities	Admin	Overheads	Total¶	
1. Industrial buildings	7									
Mean cost		155	80	133	290	1279	247	618	2831	399
Standard deviation		†	†	†	199	686	200	457	822	
2. Offices	35									
Mean cost		168	118	244	446	615	870	1185	3671	517
Standard deviation		†	†	†	222	233	525	868	1347	
3. Shops	6									
Mean cost		129	132	462	300	1059	1226	1303	4610	650
Standard deviation		†	†	†	39	194	119	315	460	
4. Homes for the aged	16									
Mean cost		99	66	28	1421‡	689	(‡)	554	2789	393
Standard deviation		†	†	†	537	103		101	539	
5. Schools	12									
Mean cost		44	74	41	482‡	360	(‡)	586	1584	223
Standard deviation		†	†	†	71	62		145	191	
6. Universities	111									
Mean cost		97	75	119	358	607	462	438	2160	304
Standard deviation		†	†	†	88	203	244	96	438	
7. Laboratories	39									
Mean cost		96	185	860	445	1105	559	654	3832	540
Standard deviation		†	†	†	262	704	549	604	2845	
8. Students Hostels	31									
Mean cost		157	100	121	583	507	346	424	2207	311
Standard deviation		†	†	†	105	107	148	51	275	

(Source: BMCIS)

Notes: * Sample size is number of completed returns.

    † Standard deviations not calculated for these items since costs vary widely.

    ‡ Cleaning and admin costs combined.

    ¶ Because of the method of calculating averages the individual means need not sum to the mean total.

    § See text: discount rate 5%, life cycle 25 years.

estimates of the net present value of future running costs between £223 and £650 per 100 m² depending upon building type. The present value figures relate to the gross floor areas of the buildings. They should be used as the basis for making decisions between competing options, and should not be confused with the full year effect costs which show actual costs incurred.

The variability of running costs

5.24 The analysis above points not only to variation in running costs of buildings as a result of building type, but also to significant variation in running costs within any one building type: see the standard deviations presented in table 5.A and the range of energy usage estimates illustrated in figure 5.2.

5.25 Such extensive variation in running costs for particular building types also emerges from the analysis of a third data set. Service charge information was obtained for a total of 126 office buildings, 59 located in Liverpool, and 67 in London, of which 16 (all located in London) are air conditioned. The data refer to 1976, 1979 and 1980 and have been rebased to 1979 using BMCIS published cost indices.

5.26 Average service charges (£/100m²) for this sample are presented in table 5.B. The service charges have been based upon the service costs incurred by the owner of the building, which includes such items as cleaning common circulation areas, divided by the net rentable area. These figures should not be taken as a true cost of actual running costs for a tenant, because a tenant will incur many additional costs not included in the service charge, such as rates. The wide variation in individual costs is clear from these summary statistics and not particularly surprising. The data refer to a heterogeneous sample of buildings: their ages range from one to 139 years as at 1979, they have anything between two and 22 storeys and are between 300m² and 38,000m² gross floor area. All the buildings are owned by private sector financial institutions and occupied by multiple tenants. In addition, the buildings were not designed on the basis of a life cycle cost approach. There is, therefore, unlikely to be any consistency in the choice of finishings, heating systems or lighting systems.

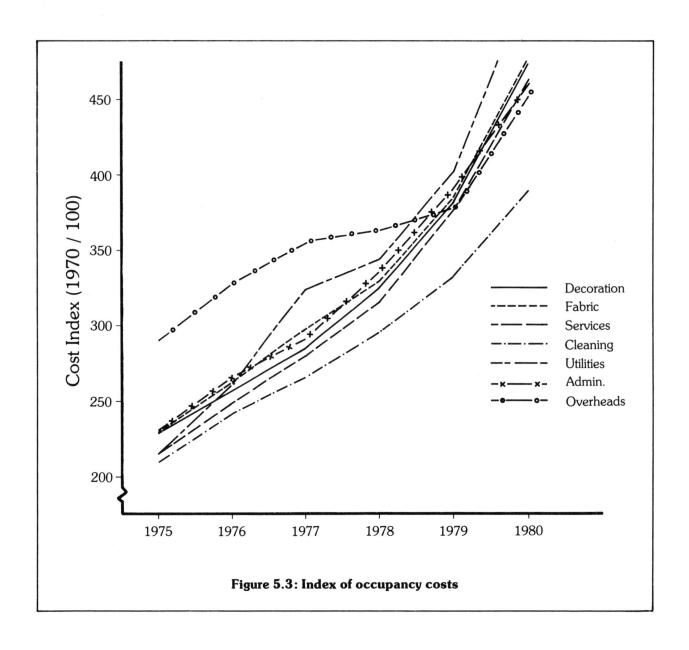

Figure 5.3: Index of occupancy costs

Table 5B: Analysis of annual service charge data

	Annual Service Charges (£/100m²)					
	Liverpool		**London** (air conditioned)		**London** (non air-conditioned)	
	Mean	Standard Deviation	Mean	Standard Deviation	Mean	Standard Deviation
Heating (1)	299	146	1025	1001	232	113
Cleaning	416	188	1136	820	688	612
Lift (2)	87	69	116	49	112	105
Electrical	356	600	1680	1544	400	480
Staff (3)	187	247	383	203	244	156
Insurance (4)	95	63	182	97	208	136
Repairs and decorations (5)	161	131	204	143	670	184
Refuse and waste disposal	32	26	59	8	95	123
Sundries	55	94	387	407	183	462
Management	94	50	297	157	212	168

(Source: confidential information provided to the authors.)
Notes: 1. All heating costs, including staff required to maintain heating systems.
2. Lift maintenance costs.
3. Security, porterage and cleaners.
4. Excluding users' contents insurance.
5. Excluding decoration of building users' walls and floors.

5.27 Investigations were made to determine whether any relationship could be identified between various of the service charges detailed in table 5.B and the physical characteristics of the building: age, size, number of floors. Such relationships have been suggested by other work. For example, the Building Research Establishment reported on quite a strong connection between energy usage and building age for certain building types.

5.28 No such relationship could be found for the office building sample but this is not to say that such relationships do not exist. Rather it suggests that data have to be selected for analysis in a much more structured way. Building aspect, user function, types of external cladding, and many other features all carry implications for running costs. Strong statistical techniques can be applied only if data are stratified according to such cost significant parameters.

5.29 A further point that emerges from table 5.B is the sharp contrast between costs of air conditioned and non-air conditioned offices. Some of the differences in costs indicated in the table are more apparent than real. Thus the differences in costs of repairs and decorations, staff, and refuse and waste disposal between these sub-samples are not statistically significant. There is, however, a clear difference of anything up to a factor of four in heating and electrical costs between air conditioned and non-air conditioned buildings. More detailed investigation suggested that this arises because the operation and maintenance of air conditioning systems demand more operations staff in addition to any extra energy demands they impose.

5.30 Two important conclusions can be drawn from this discussion. Firstly, it would appear that running costs are not 'given' for any selected building type. Significant variation remains in exhibited performance, at least part of which is rooted in design decisions. In other words, there is potential for reduction in running costs and total life cycle costs by the application of life cycle cost techniques.

5.31 Secondly, work remains to be done in identifying the cost significant parameters, noted above, by which historical data should be stratified for life cycle cost purposes. It was noted in previous paragraphs that the surveyor should select buildings of 'similar' types for cost estimation. The discussion in this chapter indicates that data homogeneity requires not only that 'offices' should be used as sources of historical data when estimating running costs for an office, but that offices with particular configurations – e.g. age, type of construction, number of storeys – should be used.

5.32 There remains, of course, the question of how historical data might be obtained. The text has concentrated upon published data and shown that these sources, while useful, are not of themselves adequate for life cycle cost purposes. Nevertheless, just as experience in the application of life cycle cost will improve data drawn from specialist suppliers and model building, so experience and increased use of sources such as BMCIS can be expected to improve the usefulness of these data.

5.33 A further potentially rich source of historical information is data collected by those who own and run current buildings but do not offer their data to BMCIS. It was noted in chapter 3 that such data are essential input to life cycle cost analysis and life cycle cost management. They are moreover, a potentially invaluable source of data for life cycle cost planning.

Conclusions

5.34 A number of important inferences follow from the analysis in this chapter. Firstly, it is clear and was to be expected that the relative impact of running costs by building elemental category is somewhat different from the relative impact of initial costs. Several particularly important cost areas emerge – exterior closure, interior construction, heating, ventilating, air conditioning, and electrical systems – from which benefits will be derived by the early and continued application of life cycle cost techniques.

5.35 Secondly, it is to be expected that life cycle costs and the functional distribution of these costs will differ significantly with building type and the building user. This implies that a decision that may generate significant life cycle cost savings for one type of building may give rather lower cost savings if implemented for other building types. It further implies that the development of an historical data base on running costs must be stratified by building type.

5.36 Thirdly, wide variations in functional occupancy costs were identified within particular building types. As has been stated, this is to be expected given that the buildings from which the data were drawn constitute heterogenous samples, even within particular building types. Life cycle costs will be affected significantly, not only by whether a building is an office, factory or some other building type, but also by design decisions, precise occupancy functions and so on. Without this latter type of information, it is unlikely that any consistency will be identified in historical data. Rarely will two very similar buildings have identical running costs.

5.37 This leads to the fourth and final point. It was stated in the introduction to this chapter that life cycle cost techniques require reliable data if they are to be implemented effectively and to generate usable results. Many of these data will be obtained from suppliers of particular building components and building services, but many others will have to be estimated from historical data. It is an unfortunate fact that the current sources of historical data do not have a sufficiently wide coverage to allow their effective use for life cycle cost calculations. The BMCIS statistics are a useful starting point, but consideration must be given to the design of data capture systems that relate running costs much more closely to individual building functions and components.

N.B. The next chapter presents one such system for collecting and using historical data and chapter 7 discusses methods for estimating particular operating costs. In both cases the analysis should be treated as a preliminary set of guidelines rather than a definitive set of proposals. In addition, it is worth emphasising that there is no substitute for actual operating experience.

Chapter 6

Key Points

- In the same way that quantity surveyors are able to forecast construction prices at the early design stages of a project, knowledge of running costs will be acquired with the benefit of experience (para. 6.1).

- Forecasting tends to be an art, not an exact science; nevertheless it is an area of decision making which cannot be left to go by default (para. 6.3).

- When preparing an LCCP attention should be focused on those elements which are likely to have the most significant impact upon running costs (para. 6.4).

- LCCP and FYEC are forecasting for proposed buildings, whereas LCCA and LCCM are concerned solely with existing buildings (para. 6.6).

- Any piece of information about a building should be collected only if there is a perceived value in doing so (para. 6.7).

- The problem of access to data is a key issue, as running cost data are not readily available (para. 6.10).

- LCCM is designed to ensure that the building is efficiently utilized. The monitoring should not be an inquisition process designed to castigate decision-makers (para. 6.20).

- The life cycle concept by itself does not make the decisions. Decisions are made by *people*. In so doing they must be expected to use a set of values of which the numerical results are only part. There is no substitute for professional skill and judgement (para. 6.35).

6

A practical approach to life cycle costing for construction

Introduction

6.1 This chapter examines some of the practical aspects of using life cycle costing when examining the running costs of complete buildings. In view of some of the problems outlined in the previous chapters, the reader at this stage may be feeling concerned at the difficulties of comparing complete buildings to evaluate life cycle costs. However, in the same way that quantity surveyors are able to forecast construction prices at the very early design stages of a proposed building, a similar knowledge will be acquired with the benefit of experience to deal with the life cycle and running cost aspects of buildings.

Initial problems

6.2 A fundamental aspect of life cycle cost planning is that it embodies forecasting, the purpose of which is to provide information for decision-making. All organisations make forecasts, although some do not use formal or scientific methods. In particular, quantity surveyors in their professional role are constantly making forecasts of market activity, and cost trends.

6.3 However, the fact remains that there is no infallible way to predict the future; forecasting tends to be an art, not an exact science. It is, nevertheless, an area of decision-making which cannot be left to go by default. Forecasting will not guarantee correct decisions, but it will improve the basis on which decisions are made. Thus an LCCP will give a clearer vision of the future than could be achieved by intuition alone. The effort will be justified even if it merely leads to the rejection of a few demonstrably wrong decisions.

6.4 The main role of the quantity surveyor when preparing an LCCP is to focus attention on those elements of the building which are likely to have the most significant impact upon the running costs. The objective is to ensure that the client obtains value for money from both an initial cost and a total cost approach.

6.5 When considering the total cost approach, it is essential to draw clear distinction between what could happen, what should happen, and what will happen. Obviously, clients are interested in what will happen. However, buildings are used in a variety of ways, and the distinction between a feasible use and what actually occurs involves a complicated network of human decisions, most of which are taken by people who may not have been directly involved in the design process. For example, the building might be cleaned at night which will necessitate lighting the building for the cleaners, whereas the design team may have assumed that cleaning would take place in the morning when no artificial lighting would be required.

6.6 In essence, LCCP and FYEC are forecasting the future for proposed buildings or systems. LCCA and LCCM, on the other hand, are concerned solely with existing buildings and endeavouring to make better use of existing resources. Whilst some quantity surveyors are already involved with the management aspects of buildings, this is likely to be a new venture for the vast majority.

6.7 LCCA involves capturing historical running costs, measurement, and performance data on existing buildings or systems. These data are not inexpensive to collect and analyse. As a result a piece of information on a building should only be collected if there is a perceived value in doing so.

6.8   Table 6.A shows the relationship between the data requirements of LCCA and those of LCCP for a complete building. As was mentioned in chapter 5, historical data collected from records or drawings will be influenced by a number of variables. For example, the annual fuel cost of running a heating system can be calculated from the fuel bills. However, it is difficult to deduce the design characteristics of the building or the occupancy pattern from these data. When using them as a price source for LCCP, a reasoned approach as to whether the historical data are strictly comparable with the proposed building is therefore required. Advice should be sought from the client on the proposed occupancy, because the quantity surveyor has little or no control over how the building will be used.

Table 6A: Relationship between the data requirements of life cycle cost analysis and life cycle cost planning

Item	LCCA	LCCP
Description of the building, location and consultants	Required	Required
Measurement Floor area Window area Wall area Roof area Any detailed elemental areas as required	Measurement from drawings or on site * * * * *	Measurement from drawings * * * * *
Performance (annual)	Actual records (possibly more than one year)	Estimated (quantity surveyor or expert advice)
Maintenance (annual) – Includes routine maintenance and minor repairs **Maintenance (non-annual)** – Alteration/adaptation/replacement	Actual records on component lives and planned maintenance. (Possibly more than one year)	Estimated (quantity surveyor)
Operations cost (annual)	Actual records (possibly more than one year)	Estimated (quantity surveyor)
Condition of building	Site visit to determine condition of elements	As specified
Discount rate, inflation rate, life cycle	Not applicable	Required

6.9   A further word of caution is that while a building must be seen as a complex system, there is an imperfect understanding of the full set of interrelationships and interdependencies between the components of that system. For example, in the case of window design, energy usage is not simply dependent upon the superficial window area; it is also affected by factors such as internal and external temperature differential, type of glazing, exposure, orientation, building usage, and location.

6.10   In most instances a detailed LCCA at level 3 (see chapter 3) is likely to be undertaken only as a commission from a client. Furthermore, quantity surveyors will not have access to operations and maintenance cost records unless they are engaged on a project for the client. The problem of access to the data is a key issue. Unlike cost planning, where the quantity surveyor has access to the cost information in the bill of quantities, running cost data are not readily available. Even where access is given, because the data have been collected for reasons other than LCCA, they will often be presented in a format which does not allow full extraction of all the relevant cost elements for LCCA.

Cost relationships

6.11   Some mention has already been made of the influence of the way a building is used and its impact upon the running costs. Data on buildings occupied for 24 hours a day cannot be compared with buildings with 10-11 hour occupancy cycles. Similarly, data on buildings with high staffing levels, such as security and caretaking staff, must be recognised as such.

6.12 The tendency when dealing with any aspect of cost, is to use a unit of measurement as the basis for comparison, either as a cost per m² of the gross floor area or as a cost for the relevant unit quantity. This practice is also followed in life cycle cost. The life cycle cost components can be considered as:

● Area related – where the cost is related to the area, *e.g.* cleaning.

● Use or function related – where the user is the predominant influence on cost, *e.g.* porterage and caretaking.

● Non-area related, *e.g.* the cost of a plant engineer to maintain the plant and equipment.

● Price related – where the cost is related to the price or replacement value, *e.g.* property insurance.

6.13 Clearly many of these components are also affected by the physical characteristics of the building. A simple example serves to illustrate this point. The annual running costs of a heating system for a 5000m² building may be assumed to be as follows.

			Cost
1.	Fuel	Area related and part user related	18,000
2.	Maintenance contracts on boiler and pumps	Non-area related	2,000
3.	Insurance on services	Non-area related	500
4.	Replacement (provision)	Non-area related	2,000
5.	Plant engineer	Non-area related	7,500

£30,000 = £6/m²gfa

6.14 As can be seen, a large proportion of these costs is not area related, limiting the usefulness of the measured cost per unit area. If a plant engineer had not been considered necessary the cost would have been £4.50/m²gfa, the assumption being that the caretaker would be responsible for start up and monitoring. Thus, in the absence of detailed information there is the possibility of data being erroneous if based solely on a unit price rate.

6.15 It is easiest to think of the costs in terms of fixed and variable costs. The fuel cost will be a variable cost related to the floor area and the use characteristics, whereas the plant engineer is a fixed cost. Many of the fixed cost items will have some relationship to the initial capital cost of an item. Insurance premiums are generally related to the replacement costs plus an allowance for professional design team fees.

6.16 Maintenance work can be divided into annual and intermittent work. Care should be taken when using historical cost data for this work. For example, redecoration of buildings is usually a constant process. In practice the planned redecoration cycles are often not followed owing to differences in climatic exposure, amount of use, and opinion as to acceptable standard. Buildings are often decorated piecemeal to avoid undue disturbance to the occupants. Therefore, when a redecoration cycle is not followed rigidly, the historical cost records for the past 3 years may not capture the cost of complete internal and external redecoration.

6.17 *Figure 6.1* illustrates the assumptions that might be made for the redecorations cost category in an LCCP. The approach is as follows.

● Estimate the superficial area and initial capital cost for the decorations.

● Estimate a cost for the annual periodic inspection and making good of the decorations.

● Determine a redecoration cycle for the various parts of the building.

- Calculate the superficial areas and estimate the cost of redecorating on the above cycle at current costs of labour and material.

- Discount future costs to a net present value (where all cash amounts are converted to an equivalent value occurring now) or to an annual equivalent value (where all cash amounts are converted to a time equivalent value occurring in a uniform amount each year over the life cycle).

Note that the cost of redecoration is estimated at current prices of labour and materials. Normally, some adjustment to the discount rate should be made for the effects of inflation (see chapter 4).

6.18 If the object of the analysis is to project actual costs on a year by year basis for the FYEC, it will make little sense to discount future expenditure. In this situation, allowance must be made for the impact of inflation on future years' expenditures if more than one year is being considered.

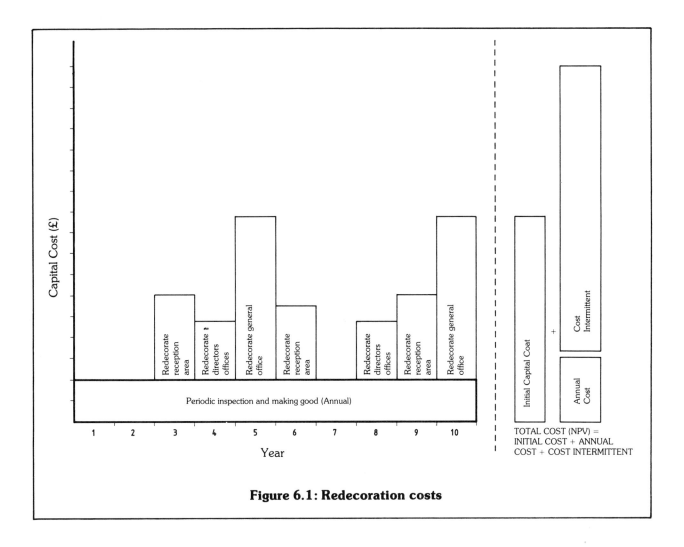

Figure 6.1: Redecoration costs

The sequence of life cycle cost analysis, life cycle cost planning and life cycle cost management

6.19 Whilst LCCA, LCCP and LCCM can be viewed as separate activities in their own right, there is a logical sequence which links them together. *Figure 6.2* shows this sequence, where the assumption is that data for an LCCP of a proposed building are based upon three similar buildings for which LCCA's are available.

6.20 The type of analysis at levels 1, 2 or 3 is solely dependent upon the extent of available design detail. The ongoing process of LCCM is to ensure that the building is efficiently utilised. It should be emphasised that the monitoring should not be an inquisition process designed to castigate decision-makers. Activity *K*

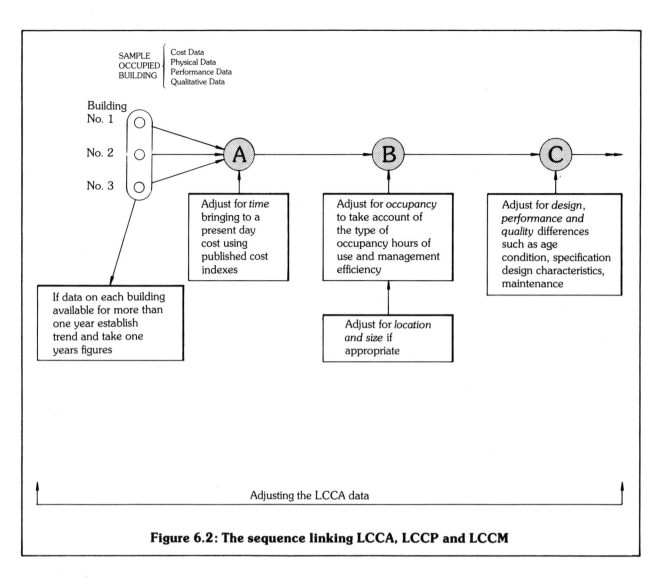

Figure 6.2: The sequence linking LCCA, LCCP and LCCM

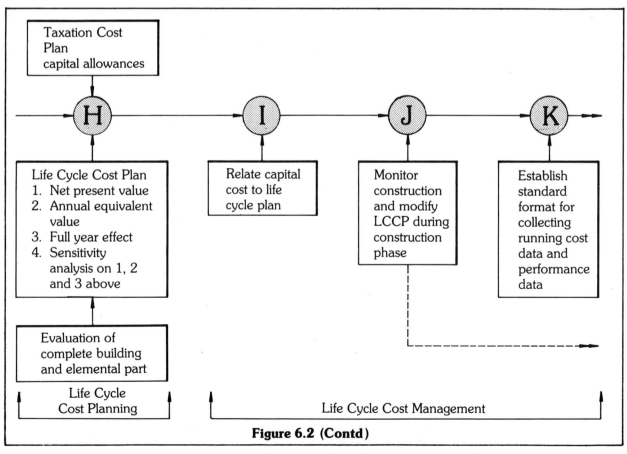

Figure 6.2 (Contd)

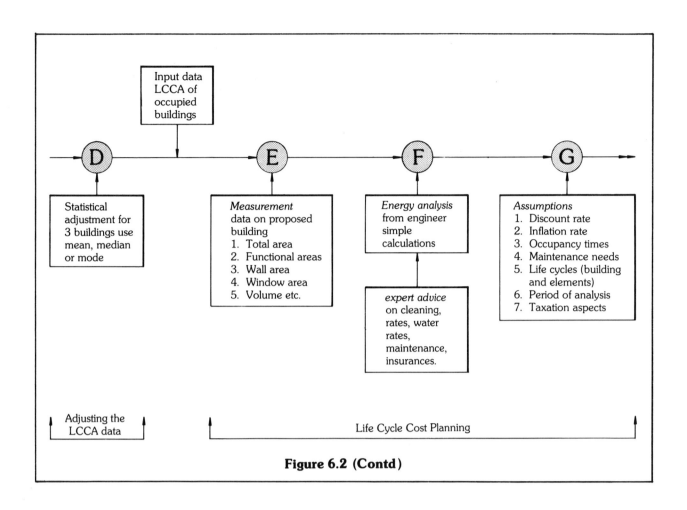

Figure 6.2 (Contd)

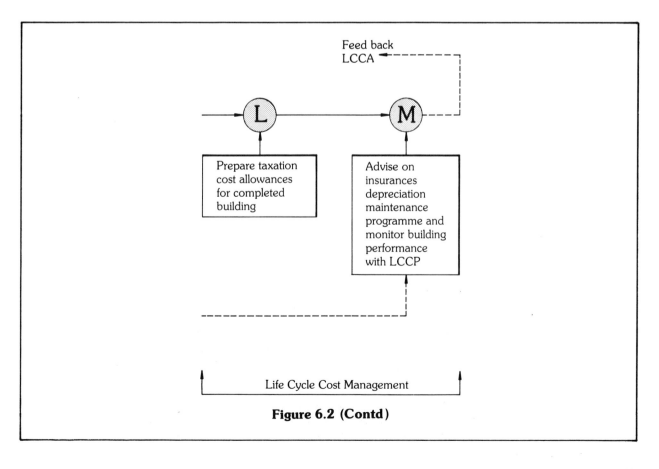

Figure 6.2 (Contd)

refers to the format and structuring of information for LCCM. As was demonstrated in chapter 3 with the concept of levels for 5 and 6, every building will have different requirements as to what data should be collected.

6.21 Activity A refers to the adjustment of the historical data by using an index. The main indices relating to running costs are published by the BMCIS. The principles for using index numbers will be familiar, but it should be noted that there are several problems in applying index numbers to cost data.

6.22 Firstly, an index number is an average. The weighting used in constructing the index number may not be precisely appropriate to the project in hand. There is no easy way of overcoming this problem. Users should exercise discretion and be as fully informed as possible about the underlying construction of the index they are proposing to use.

6.23 Secondly, different cost factors tend to inflate at different rates. Thus it may be preferable to use a number of individual cost indices, for example, for labour, energy, and cleaning, rather than an aggregate index of variable costs.

Documentation format for life cycle costs

6.24 Table 6.B shows a format for a life cycle cost plan. The data are a combination of the following.

- General descriptive
- Performance
- Measurement
- Assumptions
- Cost

6.25 These data should be used in such a way that the design team can evaluate total costs or the total cost consequences of design options. Table 6.B is only one of many possible formats for the data, and every quantity surveyor will have his own views on how best to display the information.

6.26 Section 1 gives general and descriptive data about the proposed building together with any assumptions made in the analysis. Section 2 lists building measurement data, all of which are likely to have been used in the preparation of a price forecast or capital cost plan for a proposed building. Where areas are referred to, these should be based upon the measurement rules used in the BCIS elemental categories. Mention is made of an additional section for any elemental breakdown. For example, part of the ceiling finishes area might be suspended ceilings and part painted fair face concrete. In such situations a breakdown of the areas would be useful because of differing operations and maintenance requirements.

6.27 Section 3 details annual operations and annual maintenance costs. When building up prices for inclusion in the LCCP, due account should be taken of area-related and non area-related costs. In II.1 the basis of the price is given in £/m²; had cleaning staff been direct employees then the price calculation would have been the total annual cost of employment divided by the gross floor area cleaned.

6.28 Section 4 gives information on the intermittent maintenance costs, which consist of the replacement cost of each item at current levels of labour and materials together with the replacement cycle. In most situations, only a proportion of an item will be replaced completely at a specific time; this aspect is discussed in chapter 7. In II.3 the costs are brought to a present value. Alternatively, this could easily be converted to an annual equivalent value if required, as was shown in chapter 4.

6.29 Where appropriate, all the running costs calculations should be adjusted to a net of tax figure, bearing in mind that the running costs of a building are allowable as a business expense. This will be particularly relevant for trading organizations.

Table 6B: Life cycle cost plan **Section 1**

General information

Project . . . .

Location . . . .

Date . . . .

Discount rate . . . .

Life cycle . . . .(Study period)

Sources of price data

(List LCCA (if applicable) and sources)

Description of proposed building or system

Assumptions

Occupancy . . . . .hours

Life cycles . . . .(etc.)
(List all assumptions)

Measurement

Building data

Gross floor area ....m² (give schedule of
                                                areas if applicable)
Circulation space area ....m²

Ground floor area ....m²

Volume ....m³

Upper floor area ....m²

Roof area ....m²

Wall area (net) ....m²

Windows and external
  door area (net) ....m²

Internal walls and
  partitions area ....m²

Internal door area ....m²

Wall finishes area ....m²

Ceiling finishes area ....m²

Fittings and furnishings ....nr

Sanitary appliances ....nr

Water installation
  (draw off points) ....nr

Site works ....m²

(Use separate sheet for any elemental breakdown required)

Design data

No. of occupants ....nr

Occupants/m² gross floor area ....

Net/gross floor area ....%

(Give brief specification)

II.1 Operations costs (annual)

Inflation rate ....

Inflation adjusted discount factor ....
(List items for different inflation rates)

Item	Quantity	Basis of price	Cost	£/m² (gross floor area)	Present value factor	Present value
e.g. Cleaning (Frequency: daily except weekends)	5000 m² 3500 m² Carpet 1500 m² Wood block	Cleaning contractor £6/m² Carpet £7/m² Wood block		6.30		

II.2 Maintenance costs (annual)

Inflation rate ....

Inflation adjusted discount factor ....

Item	Quantity	Basis of price	Cost	£/m² (gross floor area)	Present value factor	Present value
e.g. Replacement of light bulbs at 2000 hrs.	500 nr	Labour Materials £400 Plant		0.08		

II.3 **Maintenance/replacement/alteration costs (intermittent)**							
Item	**Quantity**	**Maintenance/ replacement cost (unit rate)**	**Interval (years)**	**Proportion to be replaced**	**Cost £**	**Present value factor**	**Present value**

II.4 **Sundries**
Building and engineering – architects, surveyors and engineers charges.

III **Taxation (private sector)**
1. Adjustment for taxation on running costs.
2. Capital allowances on buildings and plant and equipment.
3. Value Added Tax.

Assumptions and calculations.

6.30 Table 6.C is the summary section for the life cycle cost plan. A similar format can also be used for an LCCA. The main differences being as follows.

● The costs will be the actual not estimated costs incurred.

● The costs will not be discounted.

● The measurement data will be based upon the actual dimensions of the building.

● Performance measurements will be given.

● There will be some indication of the condition of the building and elements.

Measurement information

6.31 Tables 6.B and 6.C use the categories developed in chapter 3 as the basis for classifying running cost information. Certain measurement data are also required to make these categories meaningful for cost purposes.

6.32 Table 6.D shows life cycle data requirements for some of the categories. To avoid unnecessary duplication in the text, not all the categories have been shown.

6.33 As an example, if the rates category (1C) is considered, information on the rateable value of the building and the local rate poundage is required. The resultant figure could then be quantified as a cost per m^2 of the gross floor area, a cost per m^2 of the net lettable area (if it was a speculative development), or a cost per employee who was employed in the building.

Conclusions

6.34 This chapter has concentrated on some of the practical issues of using life cycle costing.

Table 6C: Life cycle cost plan summary

Project . . . .

Location . . . .

Date . . . .

Costs	Estimated target costs	Target cost per m² gross floor area	Present value
I. **Capital costs**			
e.g. Substructure			
Superstructure			
Finishings			
Fittings and furnishings			
Total capital costs			
II. **Running costs**			
II.1 **Operations costs**			
e.g. Energy			
Cleaning			
Rates			
Insurances			
Security and health			
Staff			
Management and administration			
Land charges			
Total operations costs			
II.2 **Maintenance costs (annual)**			
e.g. Main structure			
Internal decorations			
External decorations			
Total maintenance costs (annual)			
II.3 **Maintenance/replacement/ alterations costs (intermittent)**			
e.g. Main structure			
Internal decorations			
External decorations etc.			
Total maintenance/replacement/ alteration costs (intermittent)			
II.4 **Sundries**			
Total sundries			
Total running costs			
III **Additional tax allowances**			
Total additional tax allowances			
IV **Salvage and residuals**			
Total salvage and residuals			

Costs	Estimated target costs	Target cost per m² gross floor area	Present value
V Occupancy costs List assumptions			
Total occupancy costs			

Total present value of life cycle costs	
Annual equivalent value of life cycle costs	
Full year effect costs (basis of calculation to be stated)	

It should be stated that when using the above formats to prepare an FYEC, adjustments must be made for inflation and any intermittent costs.

6.35 It should be borne in mind that life cycle costing is very largely a numerical and analytical concept which will quantify only those things that can be quantified. Other factors, such as the occupancy costs of staffing a facility, are difficult to quantify.

6.36 By itself life cycle costing does not make the decisions. Decisions are made by people. In so doing, they must be expected to use a set of values of which the numerical results will only be part. The results of an analysis may look very precise and convincing, but there is no substitute for professional skill and judgement.

N.B. Inevitably the question of professional fees for providing the life cycle costing service must be considered and this is discussed briefly in chapter 10.

Table 6D: Life cycle data requirements

Item	Measurement information
1. Operations costs	
1A Energy (Apportion fuel bill to appropriate categories)	
A1 Heating A1(i) gas A1(ii) oil A1(iii) coal A1(iv) electricity A1(v) other	A1 Engineer calculation or volume A1(i) therm A1(ii) litre A1(iii) tonne A1(iv) kWh A1(v) –
A2 Cooling A2(i) electricity	A2 Engineer calculation or volume A2(i) kWh
A3 Hot water A3(i) gas A3(ii) oil A3(iii) coal A3(iv) electricity A3(v) other	A3 Number of occupants or hot water outlets A3(i) therm A3(ii) litre A3(iii) tonne A3(iv) kWh A3(v) –
A4 Ventilation A4(i) electricity	A4 Engineer calculation or volume and air change rate A4(i) kWh
A5 Lift, escalators and conveyors A5(i) electricity	A5 Number of lift or conveyor installations × load assumption A5(i) kWh
A6 Lighting A6(i) electricity	A6 Amount of floor area and illumination rate required A6(i) kWh no. of lighting points
A7 Building equipment and appliances A7(i) gas A7(ii) oil A7(iii) electricity A7(iv) other	A7 Number of appliances and appliance loading A7(i) therm A7(ii) litre A7(iii) kWh A7(iv) –
A8 Special user plant and equipment A8(i) gas A8(ii) oil A8(iii) electricity A8(iv) other	A7 Number of plant equipment and plant rating A8(i) therm A8(ii) litre A8(iii) kWh A8(iv) –
A9 Other	A9 –
1B Cleaning B1 Internal surface B1(i) user B1(ii) circulation	 B1 Total area × frequency of cleaning (m²) B1(i) functional user area × frequency of cleaning (m²) B1(ii) circulation area × frequency of cleaning (m²)
B2 External surfaces B2(i) windows B2(ii) external fabric	B1 Gross external area + frequency of cleaning (m²) B2(i) window area × frequency of cleaning (m²) B2(ii) remaining external fabric area × frequency of cleaning (m²)
B3 Lighting	B3 Number of lighting fittings × frequency of cleaning (no.)
B4 Laundry	B4 Appropriate service contract (lump sum) (based upon number of required hand towels)
B5 External works	B5 Gross area of external works to be cleaned (m²)

Life cycle data requirements	
Item	**Measurement information**
B6 Refuse disposal	B6 Service contract (lump sum) (local authority or commercial contractor)
B7 Other	B7 –
1C Rates C1 General rates	C1 Rateable value × local rate poundage (lump sum)
C2 Water rates	C2 Rateable value × local rate or × metered charge (lump sum)
C3 Effluents and drainage charge	C3 Rateable value × local rate + metered or calculated charge (lump sum)
C4 Empty rates	C4 Rateable value × local rate (empty) (lump sum)
C5 Other	C5 –
1D Insurances D1 Property insurance	D1 Construction price + design fees + demolition cost (lump sum) × rate £x per cent
D2 Mechanical and electrical services/combined engineering	D2 Value of mechanical and electrical services installation less boilers and pumps × rate of £x/per installation (lump sum)
D3 Boilers	D3 Value of boiler installation × rate of £x/per installation (lump sum)
D4 Electric motors and pumps	D4 Value of motors or pumps × rate of £x/per electric motor or pump (lump sum)
D6 Public liability	D6 Value of liability (lump sum)
D7 Employer's liability	D7 Value of liability (lump sum)
D8 Loss of profits or rent receivable	D8 Value (lump sum)
D9 Special perils	D9 Value × rate of £x/per special peril (lump sum)
D10 Lifts, sprinklers and boilers statutory inspections	D10 Value × number of lift, sprinkler and boiler inspections × rate of £x/per each inspection (lump sum)
D11 Other	D11 –
1E Security and health E1 Security services	E1 Service contract (lump sum)
E2 Pest control	E2 Value of contract (lump sum)
E3 Dust control	E3 Value of contract (lump sum)
E4 Other	E4 –
1F Staff	(Note: Overheads on staff might include provision of accommodation)
F1 Porterage	F1 Annual salary and overheads
F2 Caretaker	F2 Annual salary and overheads
F3 Commissionaire	F3 Annual salary and overheads
F4 Lift attendant	F4 Annual salary and overheads
F5 Gardening	F5 Annual salary and overheads

Life cycle data requirements	
Item	**Measurement information**
F6 Uniforms	F6 Allowance per annum
F7 Other	F7 –
1G Management and administration of the building G1 Building manager/occupancy manager	G1 Annual salary and overheads
G2 Plant manager/engineer	G2 Annual salary and overheads
G3 Building management consultancy fees	G3 Consultants fee allowance (lump sum or percentage fee)
G4 Other	G4 –
1H Land Charges H1 Ground rent	H1 Costs to the property user
H2 Chief rent	H2 Costs to the property user
H3 Easements	H3 Costs to the property user
H4 Other	H4 –
2. Maintenance costs	
2A Main Structure A1 Substructure	A1 Structure inspection and repair (m²)
A2 Frame	A2 Structure inspection and repair (m²)
A3 Upper floors	A3 Structure inspection and repair (m²)
A4 Roof structure/roof covering and drainage	A4 Structure inspection and repair + periodic replacement of roof elements (m²)
A5 Stair structure/stair finish/ stair balustrade	A5 Stair inspection and repair + periodic replacement of stair finish (no. of flights)
A6 External walls	A6 Structure inspection and repair (m²)
A7 Windows and external doors	A7 Inspection and repair + periodic replacement (m²)
A8 Internal walls and partitions	A8 Inspection and repair (m²)
A9 Internal doors	A9 Inspection and repair + periodic replacement (m²)
A10 Other	A10 –
2B External decorations	B1 Inspection and periodic redecoration to maintenance programme (m²)
2C Internal decorations C1 Wall decorations	C1 Inspection and periodic redecoration (m²)
C2 Ceiling decorations	C2 Inspection and periodic redecoration (m²)
C3 Fittings	C3 Inspection and periodic redecoration (no.)
C4 Joinery	C4 Inspection and periodic redecoration (m²)
C5 Other	C5 –

Chapter 7

Key Points

- Significant reductions in maintenance costs are likely to result from a life cycle cost approach (para. 7.4).

- The major problem to be overcome in applying life cycle cost techniques to building maintenance is the lack of a well-defined data base (para. 7.9).

- Data can be obtained from historical sources, specialist suppliers, and from a model building approach (paras. 7.10 to 7.15).

- Experience will improve both data and techniques in maintenance cost planning (para. 7.15).

- Rates constitute a significant cost burden and their cost implications should be examined at the inception stage (para. 7.17).

- Specialist advice on rating of plant and machinery can lead to significant cost savings (paras. 7.26 to 7.28).

- Energy cost planning is essential to cost-effective building design and use (para. 7.31).

- The main opportunity for energy cost savings lies in retrofitting the existing stock of buildings (para. 7.33).

- Historiclal data can be used as a basis for analysis for existing buildings. For new buildings, energy requirements will have to be estimated, perhaps using historical data (para. 7.38).

- Many energy estimation models are available to the quantity surveyor (para. 7.40).

- It is the people who occupy buildings who place the demands on systems that use energy (para. 7.41).

7

An examination of some operations and maintenance costs

Introduction

7.1 This chapter is divided into three sections:

Section 1 : Maintenance

Section 2 : Rates and other charges

Section 3 : Energy in buildings

7.2 These sections have been chosen for three main reasons. Firstly, in value terms they represent a high proportion of the total running costs of buildings. Secondly, energy use in buildings has become of increasing importance; there is need for surveyors to become actively involved in energy cost planning and energy management of buildings. Thirdly, surveyors should be aware of the methodology used in calculating general rates and water rates for buildings.

Maintenance

7.3 This section suggests an approach to the consideration of maintenance for life cycle cost purposes. It does not deal specifically with the design factors that cause maintenance problems, nor with the remedial aspects of defects.

7.4 One of the most difficult decisions facing building owners is the timing of different types of maintenance work in order to keep buildings up to a proper and acceptable state of repair. Several policies are available, ranging from a short term temporary repair to the undertaking of a full scale renewal. The choice of action depends on a number of factors.

● The rate of deterioration.

● The cost of different types of repair.

● The disruption and disturbance to the building occupants and time required for the repair.

● The relationship between the physical life of the repair and the required physical, functional, and economic life of the building.

As a result, significant reductions in maintenance costs are likely to result from a life cycle cost approach.

7.5 The concept of a building or building system life cycle was discussed in chapter 2. Inevitably, buildings wear out, require maintenance and repair, and must eventually be replaced, because building materials have a finite life. It should be emphasised, however, that not all of the elements of a building will deteriorate at the same rate. Some, such as the foundations, will last as long as the building itself and will require minimal corrective expenditure, while others, such as exterior paintwork, will deteriorate quite quickly and will need frequent attention. The need for maintenance work also arises because of excessive or abusive use, vandalism, faulty design, bad workmanship, poor quality material, or inaccurate specification. In addition, the appropriate maintenance programme and targets will vary with the quality of the overall building, for example a bank will require very different maintenance from a factory store.

7.6 In theory, required maintenance should be constantly reviewed and the fabric and services kept to an acceptable state of repair. Precise definition of an 'acceptable state of repair' is difficult, however, and can be expected to vary from element to element. There is a substantial difference between maintenance of plumbing, mechanical and electrical services, and maintenance of the building fabric. When a piece of machinery fails, a heating system for instance, it will generally require immediate attention if the building is to remain operational. The building fabric, on the other hand, does not usually fail catastrophically and the building can continue to be used even if the fabric has significantly deteriorated.

7.7 Essentially, maintenance repair consists of three stages: inspection, diagnosis and constructional or remedial action. For life cycle cost purposes maintenance of buildings can be classified in the following manner.

● **Maintenance of the main structure**
The main structure is exposed primarily to the natural elements and the maintenance work will probably involve inspection and routine planned maintenance. Life cycle cost can be used to determine the best form for this maintenance programme.

● **Maintenance of the finishings/fixtures/fittings**
The finishings suffer from wear and tear by the occupants and will require periodic renewal. Again, life cycle cost can be used, for instance to determine optimal intervals for renewal.

● **Maintenance of the plumbing, mechanical and electrical services**
Each of the service elements will have its own maintenance requirements. Whilst planned and preventive work will be undertaken, frequent corrective maintenance dependent upon the building age will be needed.

● **Redecorations**
Internal and external redecorations will be necessary on a planned basis. Only in exceptional circumstances will the complete building be redecorated; the more likely course is partial redecoration on a rotating basis, the redecorating programme being determined by a life cycle cost approach.

● **Maintenance of the external works**
The external works will require extensive maintenance with grass cutting, replacement of shrubs and trees, and paving.

● **Modernisation and adaptation**
This will often take place on a planned basis at a certain point in the building's life.

7.8 It can be seen that this classification is consistent with those items of maintenance detailed in levels 1, 2 and 3 in chapter 3.

7.9 While the application of life cycle cost techniques to maintenance costs will certainly generate rewards in terms of cost savings, a number of problems will arise in their implementation.

● Maintenance cost data are difficult to classify to a detailed level because of the varied nature of the work.

● Reliable information on deterioration rates is not readily available.

● The estimated repair and replacement costs are highly variable. For example, when restoring internal paintwork to as good as new condition, the cost will vary according to the age of the element. If the internal work is 5 years old it will be sufficient to wash down and paint with two coats of paint, whereas if the paintwork is 10 years old it will probably need stripping back, filling, and painting.

● The deterioration rates used by the surveyor can represent only an average. Elements may deteriorate in the same general pattern, but because all buildings are designed and used differently, there will be a corresponding difference in the replacement cycle. However, the expected renewal times are required for planning purposes.

● People's perception of an acceptable standard or quality will be different.

● There is no standard methodology for cost planning maintenance work.

7.10 Several methods can be suggested for overcoming these problems, as indicated in chapter 5. Firstly, historical data are available, particularly from the BMCIS that can be used to give a general indication of probable maintenance costs for selected building elements. It is worth noting that the greater the number of organizations who adopt a structured life cycle cost approach to maintenance, the better will be the BMCIS data bank.

7.11 Secondly, specialist materials and components suppliers should be asked to provide performance characteristics for their products. In particular, they should be able to provide reasonably accurate information on probable system life and required maintenance.

7.12 Finally, a model building approach can be adopted. For example, it is possible to adapt a technique used by the Local Government Operational Research Unit for planning hospital building maintenance. This is best described as a series of steps.

Step 1

List the maintenance elements as shown in chapters 3 and 6 at the appropriate level required.

Step 2

Apportion a unit of measurement together with the quantity for each elemental category.

Step 3

Consider each element in terms of its likely condition over the life span of the building or the time horizon of the analysis.

7.13 Table 7.A shows the age and condition table for the external doors and windows element. Five year time periods have been used in the example; however, the surveyor may choose whatever time period he feels appropriate. The figures have been chosen purely for illustrative purposes.

Table 7.A

Age (Years) Condition	0	5	10	15	20	25
1	100	80	60	40		
2		20	20	30	40	
3			20	25	30	60
4				5	30	40
	100%	100%	100%	100%	100%	100%

Condition 1 is as good as new.

Condition 2 is minor shrinkage and splitting of the timber.

Condition 3 is major shrinkage and evidence of general decay of the timber.

Condition 4 is splitting and major decay requiring replacement.

By applying this procedure systematically in all the time periods it is possible to build up a comprehensive picture of the deterioration of each element over time. (As was stated above, the deterioration rates are averages.)

Step 4

The table shows the deterioration if no maintenance work is undertaken. Allocate present day prices to the tasks involved to identify the optimum expenditure on maintenance.

7.14 The chart highlights two aspects of maintenance. Firstly, it gives a check list of items to be considered within the maintenance category. Secondly, the condition bands put a time value to the deterioration rate. The chart should, of course, be treated as a first stage in the analysis of maintenance costs using a structured model. It is, however, capable of extensive development by those professionals in the industry with the precise information and the expert skill and judgement necessary for such development.

7.15 There is no magical solution to maintenance cost planning, nor to the ways in which such planning can be implemented in practice. Planning is essential if buildings and building elements are to be chosen and operated in a cost effective way. It must be recognised, however, that the data necessary for maintenance cost planning will not always be easy to obtain. Three techniques have been suggested by which such data can be generated. The technique to be used in any given situation will be dependent upon the precise circumstances: a model building approach has certain attractions but must be supported by the collection and analysis of historical data. It must be emphasised that experience in the analysis of maintenance costs will lead to significant improvement in the quality of both data and techniques.

Rates and other charges

7.16 General rates payable to the appropriate rating authority and rates payable to the water authority are a necessary cost of occupation borne by the occupier upon taking up rateable occupation. To the occupier, the burden is large and such costs can exceed all the other running costs of a building.

7.17 Rates are thus an important aspect of the running costs which should be fully appreciated at the design stage. The rates burden cannot be avoided, but the cost implications of rates might be highly significant when making a comparison between altering an existing building or erecting a new building. At the inception stage, when the location of the proposed building has not been finally determined, there is obviously considerable opportunity for the costs of rates to be reduced, by siting the building in an area of:

● Low rateable value, and/or

● Low rate poundage.

7.18 It is beyond the scope of this book to give a precise definition of the rating system. A rigorous interpretation of the General Rate Act 1967 is necessary for any particular problems. Fortunately, the General Rate Act is very readable and generally District Valuers and the officers at the rating authority will provide help and guidance.

7.19 (S.108) General Rate Act 1967 gives any ratepayer the right to inspect and take copies of details in the Valuation List. Thus it is possible, provided the methods of measurement, interpretation and comparable factors are known on other properties, to estimate the likely rating assessments on proposed properties at the inception stage of a building scheme. This can then be used in life cycle cost calculations supplemented by any guidance the District Valuer may be prepared to give.

Rate planning: resiting the scheme in a different area

7.20 Gross value and rateable value are hypothetical rents at which the building would let. It follows that if a building is to be situated in an area where buildings command low rents, the building will have a low rating assessment. A compensating or further contrasting cost differential will occur which is dependent upon the rate poundage in the particular rating authority.

7.21 Table 7.B shows how rates payments, on a square foot basis have altered over the period 1973/4 to 1982/3. The figures relate to office blocks in London and provincial centres, using floorspace in London with an area in the range 10,000-50,000 square feet, and 10,000-20,000 square feet in provincial centres. The London offices are air conditioned whereas the provincial centres are centrally heated. The criteria adopted, although varying between London and provincial centres, are considered representative of good quality space in each location. The definition of rates includes sewerage charges but excludes water charges. The range of £1.30 per square foot in Bradford to £16.60 per square foot in the City of London is very wide; the costs of rates are now becoming a very significant proportion of total running costs.

Whilst many clients are committed to a specific site, there are instances where clients are considering alternatives. It is in these situations that life cycle costing will be useful.

Rate planning on a selected site

7.22 Presuming the site has been chosen, it is still possible to seek reduction in the rates burden by resiting buildings and uses within the sites.

Assumptions	Rateable value (RV) of whole	£100,000
	RV of car park	£10,000
	RV of A	£20,000
	RV of B	£40,000
	RV of C	£40,000

Rate poundage Rating Authority A – £1.50
Rate poundage Rating Authority B – £1.25

☐ **Rating liability as proposed**
A — RV £20,000 @ £1.50 = £30,000
B+C — RV £80,000 @ £1.25 = £100,000
Car park – not functionally contiguous as separate from site and could therefore be let separately.
Separate RV £10,000 @ £1.25 = £12,500

Total rates payment p.a. £142,500

☐ **Resite office in Rating Authority B**
Land in Rating Authority A – No charge

Offices being now an essential part of
the factory complex and included in 1.
Rateable Value may reduce to £95,000 @ £1.25 = £118,750

Car park £10,000 @ £1.25 = £12,500

£131,250

saving £11,250 p.a.

☐ **Resite car park in main complex**
Car park now part of factory complex, cannot be let separately:
RV £95,000 plus, say 75% of £10,000
New RV £102,500 @ £1.25 = £128,125

(Note saving increases in future years as rates poundage increases).

The example is tailored to suit the purpose, but clearly indicates that alternative strategies should be tested.

Rates on plant and machinery

7.23 Increasing complexity and rising capital costs of plant and machinery make it imperative to consider their impact on the rateable value of buildings, and thus on the rating assessment of real property.

7.24 There is a need to distinguish between those items within a building which qualify as plant and equipment for the purpose of capital allowances (discussed in chapter 8), however for rating purposes different criteria apply.

Table 7B

**Prime office rates
1973/4-1982/3**
(£ per square foot)

	1973/74	1974/75	1975/76	1976/77	1977/78	1978/79	1979/80	1980/81	1981/82	1982/83
City of London	3.30	4.70	7.40	8.20	8.80	8.80	9.20	11.20	14.20	16.60
Westminster	2.00	2.50	3.80	4.30	4.60	4.70	4.90	5.90	7.50	8.80
Barnet	0.50	0.70	0.90	1.00	1.10	1.10	1.30	1.50	1.80	2.10
Camden	2.10	2.70	3.90	4.40	5.00	5.10	5.80	7.50	9.70	10.40
Croydon	0.90	1.20	1.90	1.80	1.80	1.80	1.90	2.00	2.50	2.90
Hounslow	0.70	1.00	1.50	1.50	1.50	1.50	1.70	2.30	3.10	3.20
Islington	1.40	1.60	2.40	2.40	2.60	2.80	3.50	4.60	5.50	6.00
Kensington	1.70	2.00	3.00	3.00	3.40	3.60	3.80	4.70	6.70	7.90
Lambeth	1.60	2.00	2.70	2.90	3.20	3.30	4.20	6.70	7.80	7.60
Southwark	1.60	1.80	2.60	2.80	2.90	3.00	3.60	5.00	6.80	7.20
Aberdeen	0.40	0.50	0.60	0.70	0.80	1.20	1.50	1.80	2.10	2.60
Birmingham	0.60	0.80	1.00	1.00	1.10	1.10	1.20	1.50	2.00	2.20
Bradford	0.30	0.50	0.60	0.60	0.70	0.70	0.80	0.90	1.10	1.30
Bristol	0.50	0.60	0.80	0.80	0.90	1.00	1.20	1.40	1.60	1.90
Cardiff	0.40	0.60	0.80	0.90	1.00	1.00	1.10	1.30	1.50	1.70
Edinburgh	0.80	1.00	1.30	1.40	1.60	2.10	2.50	3.40	4.80	5.00
Glasgow	1.20	1.30	1.50	1.70	1.90	1.30	1.40	2.00	2.70	3.20
Hull	0.30	0.50	0.60	0.60	0.70	0.70	0.80	1.00	1.10	1.50
Leeds	0.70	0.90	1.00	1.00	1.00	1.10	1.30	1.60	2.10	2.40
Leicester	0.40	0.60	0.80	0.80	0.90	1.00	1.20	1.40	1.60	2.00
Liverpool	0.50	0.60	0.60	0.70	0.80	0.80	1.00	1.30	1.60	1.80
Manchester	0.70	0.80	1.00	1.10	1.30	1.40	1.50	1.90	2.40	2.70
Newcastle	0.70	0.90	1.20	1.20	1.20	1.40	1.60	2.10	2.70	3.00
Norwich	0.40	0.60	0.70	0.80	0.90	1.00	1.00	1.20	1.40	1.60
Nottingham	0.40	0.60	0.70	0.70	0.80	0.80	0.80	1.00	1.20	1.50
Sheffield	0.60	0.80	0.90	1.00	1.10	1.20	1.40	1.90	2.60	3.10
Southampton	0.40	0.60	0.80	0.90	1.00	1.00	1.10	1.40	1.50	1.60

(Source: *Office Rent and Rates 1973-1982*, Debenham Tewson and Chinnocks. Reproduced by courtesy.)

7.25 Fortunately, the General Rate Act 1967 lists rateable plant and machinery in Schedule 3. Under S.21.(3) a committee from time to time details all the machinery and plant which appears to fall within any of the classes within Schedule 3. Unless plant and machinery are specifically listed they are not rated nor should they be included in the buildings rating assessment. S.21.(2) gives an occupier the right to request a list of the machinery and plant which have been included in the rating assessment.

7.26 The discipline of plant and machinery rating valuation is complex and requires the services of a specialist. Potential savings are possible from using such services if, for a particular proposal:

● The rates effect could be calculated.

● A change in construction could prevent the item being rated.

7.27 As an example of the rates effect, the installation of a fire sprinkler system may have 100% capital allowance and give savings on insurance premiums, but its inclusion will increase the rating assessment and thus the cost of rates to the occupier.

7.28 The effect of construction choice is illustrated by the case of *Shell Mex and BP Ltd. v. Holyoak* [1959] WLR. The House of Lords ruled that a petrol tank lowered into brick lined pits, surrounded with sand and the whole covered in reinforced concrete was not rateable. But Lord Morton, commenting on their reasoning, stated that the position might be different if the metal cylinder were so linked with the surrounding compartment as to become one physical entity – for instance if the space were filled with concrete instead of sand.

7.29 It is usual to include plant and machinery within the overall assessment of office and shop premises on the basis that it is the plant and machinery which creates the value. For example, office floor space would not be let to a tenant on the upper floors without adequate lifts. However, with the increasing sophistication of plant and machinery, computer communications, integral telephone exchanges, and such like, this attitude may be forced to change in the future.

Other charges

7.30   Various other charges on a building can be identified.

- Environmental service charge.
- Sewerage and sewage disposal charges.
- Supply of water.
- Trade effluent charges for discharge to public sewers.
- Refuse disposal.

These charges will be related in many instances to the general rates charge and so will be affected by any design decisions that affect general rates charges. They also constitute a potentially significant cost burden and so should be identified as part of Full Year Effect Costs. Their calculation can be complex, however, and will vary with local circumstances. It is recommended, therefore, that professional advice be sought in the performance of such calculations.

Energy in buildings

7.31   Energy conservation has become critical in the planning and design of buildings owing to increasing energy prices and the threat of fuel shortages. Supplying energy will become increasingly expensive. Maintaining the current levels of demand for energy in buildings involves unprecedented economic risk due to the instability of the world energy market. Energy consumption in building systems accounts for approximately 45% of the U.K. primary energy demand. Table 7.C shows the breakdown of energy consumption within building systems for 1976. As would be expected, the highest percentage of total consumption was for space and water heating, which includes some element of cooling in commercial, institutional and industrial buildings.

Table 7C: Energy consumption in buildings (percentages)

Building Functions	Space and water heating	Cooking	Lighting	Appliances	Total percentage
Domestic	43	5	2	9	59
Commercial, Institutional	16	2	6	3	27
Industrial	11	–	2	1	14
Total buildings	70	7	10	13	100

(Source: *Energy Technologies for the United Kingdom.*)

7.32   Life cycle costing can be used by quantity surveyors to select energy conservation measures that can be taken both at the design stage of new buildings and in the retrofitting of existing buildings. Its emphasis is on determining how to allocate a given budget among competing options so as to maximise the net return, the main aim being to save energy in ways that are cost effective. This is reinforced by the Department of Energy Circular 1/75 which states: 'It is Government policy that energy conservation measures taken should be fully justified in economic terms, their cost being completely covered by the fuel saving achieved so that there is no waste of resources as a whole'.

7.33   About 75% of the present building stock in the UK, 35% of which was built before 1945, is likely to continue in use to the end of the century and beyond. Most of these buildings were designed at a time when fuel costs were much lower and the financial incentive to reduce energy consumption was much less. Each year new buildings add less than 1% to the existing building stock, and thus the main opportunity for energy conservation lies in retrofitting the existing stock of buildings. Comparing the total costs of energy conservation projects is not straightforward because of the interaction between the running cost elements. Costs which must be considered in life cycle cost in addition to energy costs are repair, replacement, maintenance and operating personnel, such as plant engineers. The fuel costs are the costs of delivered energy to the building, but these are influenced by the operations and maintenance policy of the building. For example, more expenditure on planned maintenance will improve the efficiency of equipment and reduce its energy usage. Furthermore, insurances and general rates will be influenced by an improvement in certain facilities in the building.

Life cycle cost planning and energy conservation

7.34 This section will give a broad outline of those factors to be considered when preparing a life cycle cost plan for energy conservation projects. The simplest approach is to consider a series of steps.

Step 1

Identify the various options.

Step 2

Establish the appropriate life cycle and discount rate to be used in the analysis.

Step 3

Identify all the running cost elements and likely benefits associated with the options.

Step 4

Estimate the initial capital costs of the options.

Step 5

Estimate the building's energy requirements in the light of its construction, usage characteristics, and environmental requirements.

Step 6

Estimate the energy costs, the annual operations costs, the annual maintenance and intermittent costs. Discount future costs to present values.

Step 7

Rank the options and test the sensitivity to the various assumptions underlying the estimates. For example, examine how a reduced replacement cycle for the boiler in a heating system affects the life cycle cost.

7.35 Table 7.D gives a format for a life cycle cost plan for alternative energy conservation projects. Section 1 is designed to give general information on the project together with details of any price data and assumptions made in the analysis. Section 2 is a summary of the estimated costs and present values. In the running cost categories, certain items such as fuel and heat source, have been included to illustrate the types of item within the category. The actual items for inclusion are solely at the discretion of the quantity surveyor. In this respect the appendix to chapter 3 is useful as a check list of categories and items. The level of analysis will be dependent upon the amount of information available.

7.36 Section 3 could be used to form a worksheet for section 2. It is likely that an adjustment for inflation will be required to convert the annual costs in II.1 operations costs and II.2 maintenance costs. The inflation rate and the inflation adjusted discount factor should therefore be specified. A different inflation rate may be used for each of the items. For example it might be considered that fuel prices will escalate faster than the cost of cleaning.

7.37 II.3 relates to maintenance costs that are incurred intermittently. Assumptions about the maintenance replacement and renewal cycles should be given.

Table 7D Life cycle cost plan (energy) **Section 1**

General information

Project ....

Location ....

Date ....

Discount rate ....

Life cycle .... (Study period)

Sources of price data

(List sources of price data)

Description of options

Option 1

Option 2

Assumptions

Occupancy .... (hours)

Life cycles .... (etc.)

(List all assumptions)

Costs	Option 1		Option 2	
	Estimated target costs	Present value	Estimated target costs	Present value
I **Capital costs** (List)				
Total capital costs				
II **Running costs** II.1 **Operations costs** Fuel Cleaning Rates Insurances Management and administration				
Total operations costs				
II.2 **Maintenance costs (annual)** Heat source Space heating and air treatment Ventilating system Electrical installation Gas installation Lift installation				
Total maintenance costs (annual)				
II.3 **Maintenance/replacement/alterations cost (intermittent)** Plumbing and sanitary services Heat source Space heating and air treatment Ventilating system Electrical installation Gas installation Lift installation				
Total maintenance/replacement/ alterations cost (intermittent)				
II.4 **Sundries** (List)				
Total sundries				
IV.3 **Salvage and residuals** (List)				
Total salvage and residuals				

Total present value of life cycle costs		
Annual equivalent value of life cycle costs		
Full year effect costs		
Cost per m²/gross floor area		

95

II.1 Operations cost (annual)

Inflation rate ....

Inflation adjusted discount factor ....
(List items for different inflation rates)

Item	Quantity	Basis of price	Cost	£/m² (gross floor area)	Present value factor	Present value

II.2 Maintenance cost (annual)

Inflation rate ....

Inflation adjusted discount factor ....
(List items for different inflation rates)

Item	Quantity	Basis of price	Cost	£/m² (gross floor area)	Present value factor	Present value

II.3 Maintenance/replacement/alteration costs (intermittent)							
Item	Quantity	Replacement cost	Interval (years)	Proportion to be replaced	Cost	Present value factor	Present value

Clients will also be interested in two further cost features.

● The Full Year Effect Costs for the mechanical and electrical services in a proposed building.

● A life cycle cost analysis for the services in an existing building with a view to retrofitting.

7.38 In the case of the existing building the invoices for fuel costs can be analysed, but for new buildings it will be necessary to estimate the expected energy requirements, perhaps using historical data from existing buildings.

Estimating energy requirements

7.39 The calculation of the energy requirements and heating and cooling equipment sizes in a building is very complex. It not only requires determination of the heating and cooling loads, taking into account the continually varying outside weather and the frequently varying inside load conditions, but also determination of the performance of the mechanical systems under conditions of partial load. The peak capacity requirements of equipment must be identified as well as the translation of the building operating schedules into energy demand and consumption.

7.40 The services engineer will normally provide the quantity surveyor with an estimate of the energy requirements for a proposed building. There are also a considerable number of energy estimation models available to the quantity surveyor, ranging from the highly sophisticated computer assisted models such as BEEP* through to simple empirical approaches. Many of the design data used in the models derive from the Chartered Institution of Building Services (CIBS) design guides. The model developed in the following paragraphs is intended as a simple approach which could be used at the early design stages of a project. It is not envisaged as a substitute for the expert advice provided by the services engineer.

How and why buildings use energy

7.41 One important factor that determines the energy consumption of a building is the way the building is used. It is the people who occupy buildings who place the demands on systems that use energy. The reality of such statements is often ignored in many forecasts of energy use. It will be apparent that the hours of operation of the building have a significant impact upon the energy use. A hospital or hotel is used throughout the year for 24 hours a day, whereas a school is used for approximately 7 hours a day for 40 weeks of the year.

7.42 Comparisons of the energy consumption of similar functional building types on the basis of installed capacities of heating, ventilating, air-conditioning, lighting and other electrical equipment can be misleading, because the amount of energy used in a building will be a function of the following.

- Temperature and humidity levels.
- The number of occupants and the task they perform.
- The size, shape, and zoning.
- Ambient weather conditions.
- The window/wall ratio, the type of glazed areas and the provision of shading.
- The U values of the building fabric which affects heat loss, heat gains, and the thermal response.
- The lighting levels.
- Air movement and ventilation rates.
- The hours of operation of systems and components.
- The orientation (the effects of winds and solar heat gain in relation to the shape).
- The presence of an energy management programme.
- Heat losses and heat gains for each building zone.
- The different fuels used.
- The extent of appliances and machinery.
- The presence of heating control systems.
- The number of lifts.
- The operating efficiencies of the heating and cooling equipment and distribution systems.

* BEEP : Building Energy Estimating Programme available through the Electricity Council.

7.43 This variability is illustrated by table 7.E which shows the results of a study conducted by the BMCIS (1979) on the energy consumption for nine office buildings and seven university buildings on a heat supplied basis.

Table 7E: Fuel consumption for office and university buildings

Building	type	1973/74	1974/75	1975/76	1976/77	1977/78
Office	1	1,164	1,387	1,321	–	–
	2	781	845	836	–	–
	3	1,139	954	989	–	–
	4	1,637	789	1,014	–	–
	5	–	664	612	539	–
	6	–	–	–	1,705	–
	7	–	–	346	345	449
	8	–	900	799	1,222	–
	9	–	–	981	1,073	1,108
University	1	1,502	1,637	1,490	1,457	–
	2	1,383	1,443	1,577	–	–
	3	862	1,028	1,054	–	–
	4	1,490	1,492	1,371	1,509	1,435
	5	1,123	1,250	1,270	–	–
	6	1,169	1,006	944	–	–
	7	–	884	935	912	–

(Figures are in therms per annum/100m² gross floor area)
(Source: BMCIS)
Conversion: 1 Therm = 29.3 kWh
　　　　　　1 kWh = 3412 Btu

7.44 The buildings are of varying ages and located throughout the UK. The university buildings sample has both residential and teaching areas. The arithmetic mean for all the years of the offices sample is 944 Therms/100 m² (277 kwh/m²) and the universities sample 1,260 Therms/100 m² (369 kwh/m²). There is variability of energy consumption between individual buildings and from year to year. It is interesting to note that there was reasonable consistency between the total average degree days but not between the energy consumption for the buildings. Table 7.F shows the yearly total degree days for the financial years 1973/74 to 1976/77.

Table 7F: Total average degree days for financial years

Year	1973/74	1974/75	1975/76	1976/77
Degree Days	2281	2300	2330	2332

(Source: Department of Energy)
Note: The average degree days are calculated by averaging the monthly totals for the heating season. There will be a variation in degree days for different parts of the country.

7.45 Estimating the energy requirements for a building is as problematical as estimating a construction price for a proposed building at the design stage. Prices are influenced by the market place; energy use is influenced by the weather, occupancy patterns, and other variables. As an illustration, theoretically, the temperature in all rooms of a building having the same function should be controlled exactly to the same value. However, in reality the temperature in any one room swings about a mean owing to variations in occupancy, solar gain, and so on. Temperature fluctuations should be kept to a minimum. A rise of 1°C in mean room temperature from 18° to 19°C is accompanied by a rise of approximately 10% in fuel consumption for space heating.

An energy model

7.46 The energy model outlined below seeks to satisfy two requirements.

● The estimated energy demand for the building expressed in kWh/m² gross floor area.

● The expected cost of providing energy for the building which can be used in life cycle cost planning.

7.47 The energy demand for a non air-conditioned building is the sum of the following.

- Net heating requirement – calculated from the total design heat loss from the fabric and ventilation minus heat gain from the occupants, lighting, miscellaneous equipment.

- Heating for hot water service.

- Electrical energy required for lighting, lifts, pumps and miscellaneous equipment.

Certain basic data are required to develop the model.

- Gross floor area.

- Ground floor area.

- Cubic volume.

- Roof area.

- Net external wall area.

- Net external glazed area for walls and roof.

- Number of occupants of the building.

- U values of external walls, roof, floor and glazing.

- Orientation.

- Design temperatures – the usual design temperature during occupied periods is 22°C (Summer), 19°C (Winter), and 15.5°C during unoccupied periods.

- Ventilation and infiltration.

- Lighting levels – levels of lighting are generally described in *lux*:

  Examples are:

  > 400 lux – 21.52 W/m² (primary energy terms)
  > 600 lux – 26.90 W/m²
  > 800 lux – 37.66 W/m²
  > 1000 lux – 45.73 W/m²

  (based on a 5 day week occupancy.)

- Number of zones for the building.

- Occupied periods of the building – calculations must be made to ascertain the heating hours and lighting hours per annum, and the number of working days in the heating season.

  Examples are:

	Heating hours per annum	**Lighting hours per annum**
Schools	1,731	400
Offices	4,043	586

- Hot water services – usually based upon the number of occupants, and the typical daily supply of hot water per person.

- Miscellaneous electrical power requirements.

- Fuels, and costs of fuels to be used.

- Degree days appropriate to season and locality concerned.

7.48 An approach detailed below shows the use of some of these factors. It must be emphasised that the simplified model underlying the approach shown in table 7.G relates to a heated only, non-zoned building. It attempts purely to show the principles of calculation. A more detailed model, which it was not felt appropriate to repeat in this book, can be found in 'Guidelines for Environmental Design and Fuel Conservation in Educational Buildings', Department of Education and Science, Architects and Building Branch, Design Note 17 (1981); or in the CIBS Building Energy Code, Part 2.

7.49 Quantity Surveyors should be familiar with the normal heat loss calculation for estimating plant capacity, that is:

Total heat loss = Fabric loss + Ventilation loss

$$QD = (\Sigma U \times A \times \triangle td) + (Volume \times Ventilation\ allowance \times \triangle td)$$
(7.I)

QD = Design heat loss (W)
U = U value (thermal transmittance coefficient) W/m²°C for each individual external element
A = Area in m² of the element
$\triangle$td = Design temperature difference °C
Volume = volume of space in m³
Ventilation allowance = 0.33 × air change rate per hour in W/m³°C

$$Total\ heat\ loss\ per\ °C = \frac{QD}{\triangle td}$$
(7.II)

7.50 This total heat loss calculation is based on a nominal 'worst' outside temperature to ensure that the plant can cope with this condition.

7.51 A calculation of annual energy requirement must involve an assessment of average outside conditions, the length of time the plant is operational and the effect of casual gains (mainly due to occupants, lighting, solar gain and machines). This leads to the 'Degree-days' concept, explained above.

The effects of building structure and varying internal gains are taken into account by varying the base temperature (this is the external temperature at which the design internal temperature can be maintained by the miscellaneous gains without the heating on). For an office building of traditional construction, the base temperature can be taken as 15.5°C and the CIBS Guide gives degree-day data to this base for fourteen localities (table B18.12), together with a method of correcting the data for other building types (with differing base temperatures).

7.52 The annual energy use for a building continuously occupied throughout the heating season is then:

$$\begin{matrix} Annual\ energy\ use \\ in\ kWh \end{matrix} = \frac{QD}{\triangle td} \times \frac{24 \times D}{1000}$$
(7.III)

Where D is the annual degree days to base 15.5°C. The 24 converts days into hours and the 1,000 converts watts into kilowatts. (It should be noted that equation (7.III) relates to a building occupied 24 hours a day.)

Intermittent operation

7.53 However, most buildings are intermittently occupied and the annual energy requirement will be reduced by switching the plant off overnight and at weekends. Correction factors must thus be included for the length of the working week and the working day. It may be less obvious that the effects of the response of the building and the heating system must also be considered, this is because they will affect the warm up and cooling down as the heating is switched on and off. For the basic traditional building suggested above, with hot water heating, the correction factors may be:

- Length of working week, 5 day week   0.8

- Response of building and plant
  Medium structure of plant   0.8
  Length of working day, 8 hours/day   1.0

Thus for intermittent operation:

$$\begin{matrix} Annual\ energy\ use \\ in\ kWh \end{matrix} = \frac{QD}{\triangle td} \times \frac{24 \times D \times K}{1000}$$
(7.IV)

K being the product of the three correction factors as given by the CIBS Guide, chapter B18. (In this case K = 0.64.)

Annual fuel use and cost

7.54 When the annual energy use has been obtained, the annual fuel use is given by:

$$\frac{\text{Annual energy use in kWh}}{\text{Calorific value of the fuel}} \div \text{seasonal efficiency of plant}$$

remembering that compatible 'units' must be used. Calorific values are obtainable from fuel suppliers. The annual energy use above has been calculated in kWh. This may be converted to the heat units quoted by the supplier, if necessary, according to the following:

$$
\begin{aligned}
1 \text{ kWh} &= 3.6 \text{ mJ} \\
&= 0.3412 \text{ therms} \\
&= 3412 \text{ Btu}
\end{aligned}
$$

7.55 Seasonal efficiencies are quoted by the CIBS (table B18.18) and are less than the normally quoted efficiencies owing to operation under partial load.

7.56 Annual cost is then obtained given knowledge of the unit cost of the fuel. The fuel costs must be carefully studied when annual running costs are being calculated, as the tariffs of some supply boards vary considerably. For example, electricity supply tariffs are affected by the class of consumer (domestic, industrial or commercial) and the size of the consumer's load and pattern of demand. Supplies during off-peak periods will have special low price tariffs.

7.57 Table 7.G shows a format for structuring the data in estimating an energy requirement for a building, together with a simple example for calculating the energy requirement for heating. The example in chapter 9 shows the approach in more detail.

Table 7G: Estimated energy requirement (for heated only buildings)

General building data	
Gross floor area	m²
Ground floor area	m²
Roof area	m²
Wall area (net)	m²
Glazed wall area (net)	m²
Glazed roof area	m²
Cubic volume	m³
Total envelope area	m²

Table 7G (Contd)

Design data

No. of occupants ....

Occupants/m² gross floor area ....

U values W/m²°C

Wall ....

Roof ....

Glazing ....

Floor ....

Air change rate .... air change/hrs

No. of hours occupancy .... hrs/day/week/p.a.

Lighting levels

Area 1 .... lux

Area 2 .... lux

Fuel

Heating .... type

Hot water .... No. of outlet points

Electrical equipment and
power requirements .... kWh/m²

Costs

Gas .... p/therm

Electricity .... p/unit*

Oil .... p/litre

---

* For a detailed discussion on cost conversion, see *"Guidelines for Environmental Design and Fuel Conservation in Educational Buildings"* – Department of Education and Science, Design Note 17 (1981).

Annual cost

Simplified example of the annual heating cost calculation for a building

(1) Design heat loss per m² | W/°Cm² |

(2) Degree days
    (see CIBS Table B18.12) | °C days |

(3) Annual energy requirement
    (assuming continuous operation)
    $$\frac{(1) \times (2) \times 24}{1000}$$ | kWh/m² |

(4) Annual energy requirement
    (assuming specified use)
    (3) × 0.64 | kWh/m² |

(5) Calorific value of fuel
    (From supplier or data book)

(6) Seasonal efficiency
    (From CIBS Table B18.18)

(7) Fuel cost
    (From supplier)

£/unit/charge
litre

(8) Annual heating cost

$$\frac{(4)}{(5)} \times \frac{100}{(6)} \times (7)$$

£

* Degree days are the daily difference in °C between a base temperature (such as 15.5°C) and the 24 hour mean outside temperature when it falls below the base temperature summed over a given period, usually a month, at the heating season. Degree day figures provide a climatic correction for calculations and make possible an allowance for weather variations to be made when comparing the plant for one heating season with the same plant during a previous period.

Chapter 8

Key Points

- The taxation aspects of buildings are often imperfectly understood by the surveying profession, and yet can have a fundamental effect on the true costs of the construction and operation of buildings (para. 8.1).

- In general any expenditure incurred as a running cost of a building is deduc ible against liability for tax (para. 8.4).

- It is to be expected that buildings will be written down for tax purposes much more quickly than for accounting purposes (para. 8.9).

- A company is interested in calculating its trading profit as accurately as possible, whereas the government is more interested in regulating investment (para. 8.9).

- The profession needs to take a greater interest in the development of taxation cost planning as one of the professional services offered by surveyors (para. 8.39).

8

Taxation and life cycle cost

The implications of taxation and grants for life cycle cost

8.1 The taxation aspects of buildings are often imperfectly understood by the surveying profession, and yet can have a fundamental effect on the true costs of the construction and operation of buildings. Effective tax planning can turn an apparently loss making project into a profitable one, or change the ranking order of a number of project proposals or design choices. Even in the absence of such dramatic effects, effective taxation cost planning offers significant benefits for clients of the building industry. This is so because the greater the proportion of the cost eligible for tax relief, the lower the net (after tax) cost will be.

8.2 This chapter examines a number of the more important elements in the taxation of buildings. However, tax regulations change from year to year, not merely in respect of rates of tax that are applied, but also in terms of the types of building that will be eligible for particular tax allowances. The surveyor who seeks to tax plan buildings must, therefore, become familiar with the various Finance Acts and other regulations as they apply to buildings.

8.3 The distinction between capital expenditure and revenue expenditure must constantly be borne in mind.

Capital expenditure – a term which is used to refer to money expended in acquiring assets, or in the permanent improvement of, or the addition to, or the extension of, existing assets, which are intended for use in the carrying out of business operations. These assets should be expected to have a useful life of more than one year.

Revenue expenditure – expenditure charged against expense in the period of acquisition. This term is used to refer to all expenditure which cannot be debited to an asset account.

8.4 In the calculation of a company's liability to tax, revenue expenditure is deductible before settling the amount of profit liable to tax. In the context of life cycle costing, the items that are considered a business expense are rent, energy, cleaning, general rates, water rates, lighting, security, insurances, staff, maintenance, and management expenses of the building, repairs to the building and plant, costs of renewal of plant, and writing off obsolescent plant. *In general, it may be said that any expenditure incurred as a running cost of a building is deductible against liability for tax.*

8.5 Capital expenditure, on the other hand, is not treated as a simple business expense for tax purposes. Expenditure on new buildings, or on the enlargement or betterment of an existing building is considered as capital expenditure and cannot be deducted directly in calculating tax liability. The principle appears to be that if capital receipts are not subject to income tax, then capital expenses are not allowable. (In some instances the cost of renewing worn out capital items of plant and machinery is allowable as a running cost at the time of renewal, thus providing the one exception to the principle.)

8.6 However, certain types of capital expenditure are eligible for capital allowances. The nature of these capital allowances and their life cycle cost effects are analysed in the following sections.

Capital allowances for buildings

8.7 The taxation treatment of capital expenditure on buildings is analogous to its accounting treatment: the expenditure is not deducted from profits as an ordinary expense at the time it is incurred, but depreciation allowances (known as capital allowances) are given for many, but not all, types of such capital expenditure. Here, however, the similarity ends. There need be no close connection between depreciation allowances entered in the profit and loss account or the balance sheet, and the depreciation or capital allowances taken for taxation purposes.

8.8 In an accounting context, depreciating an asset means spreading the cost over its estimated useful economic life. For example, this might be by the straight line or linear method of depreciation, which involves dividing the cost, less estimated scrap value, of an asset by the estimated economic life. The charging of depreciation simultaneously reduces the recorded amount of the fixed asset concerned in the balance sheet and the net profit of the company.

8.9 For taxation purposes, on the other hand, different rules apply. Capital allowances are available only on selected types of building, but then the majority of the allowances can be taken in the early life of the building. Thus, it is to be expected that buildings will be written down for tax purposes much more quickly than for accounting purposes. The main reason for this is that while a company in reporting to its shareholders is interested in calculating its trading profit as accurately as possible, the government is more interested in regulating investment. The underlying philosophy is that the government wants companies to invest in plant and equipment to improve the nation's economic performance.

8.10 Essentially, capital allowances are available on new industrial buildings, hotels, industrial and commercial buildings in Enterprise Zones, agricultural buildings, and small workshop buildings. Various Finance Acts and subsequent case laws define the criteria by which a building qualifies for the allowance. In the interest of brevity, only industrial buildings have been considered further within this section.

8.11 To determine whether an industrial building qualifies for capital allowances, and the precise form of such allowances, consideration must be given to the type of trade and the nature of the building. The term *industrial building or structure*, means a building or structure in use for any of the following purposes.

- A trade carried on in a mill, factory or other similar premises.

- A trade which consists in the manufacture of goods or materials or the subjection of goods or materials to any process.

- A trade which consists in the storage of goods or materials which are to be used in the manufacture of other goods or materials; or of goods or materials which are to be subjected, in the course of a trade, to any process; or of goods or materials which, having been manufactured or produced or subjected to any process, have not yet been delivered to any purchaser; or of goods or materials on their arrival by sea or air into the U.K.

8.12 The industrial building or structure does not include any building or structure in use as, or as part of, a dwelling house, retail shop, showroom, or office. However, where part of the industrial building is used for a non-qualifying activity, such as an office building attached to the factory, provided that 10% or less of the capital cost is attributable to that portion of the building, the whole building will be treated as industrial. The implications of this condition are discussed in more detail below. What should be clear is that, wherever possible, it is important to ensure that non-qualifying parts of the building are integrated within the whole structure to ensure the 10% waiver.

8.13 A sports pavilion used by a trader for the welfare of his employees is treated as an industrial building whether or not the trader is carrying on a qualifying activity. In addition, a building may be treated as an industrial building for some years and not for others, if it is used for different activities at different times.

8.14 The word *structure* embraces artificial works which might not properly be described as buildings, such as wells, bridges, roads, culverts, tunnels, and so on. Expenditure on the land itself is excluded from the allowance. However, the cost of demolition and the professional fees of the design team are eligible for capital allowances. Furthermore, the extension to an existing industrial building will qualify in the same manner as a new industrial building.

8.15 The allowances are generally given to the owner of a building, not the user, but a significant exception was introduced in the 1978 Finance Act. Under this Act, lessees of industrial buildings were permitted to claim capital allowances on their buildings as long as the lease exceeded 50 years and lessors agreed to forego the allowances in favour of the lessees. As a consequence, developers who are exempt from paying tax, such as Development Corporations, will now be able to pass on potentially valuable allowances to the actual tenants of industrial buildings.

8.16 Where a building qualifies for capital allowances, the general structure of these allowances is as follows.

- Initial allowance.
- Writing down allowance.
- Balancing allowance.

8.17 The initial allowance is made to a company in respect of the expenditure on the construction cost of the new building plus the professional design team fees. If a new unused building is purchased from a builder, the purchase price is eligible for the allowance. (The allowance is not available to the purchaser of a *used* industrial building.) The initial allowance available as a consequence of the 1981 Finance Act is 75% of qualifying expenditure, and a writing down allowance of 4% is given annually until the cost is written-off.

8.18 Some exceptions should be noted. In particular, on 'small' industrial units (under 2,500 ft² in the 1980 Budget, and under 1,250 ft² in the 1982 Budget) 100% capital allowance can be taken in the first year,* while a somewhat smaller initial allowance is available on hotels.

8.19 The balancing allowance is made if the building is sold for a sum in excess of the written down allowance. However, if the building is sold for a lower figure than its written down value, then a further allowance is given to make up the difference.

8.20 The life cycle cost effects of these capital allowances are significant as can be seen, for example, on a new industrial building, excluding land, that costs £1,000,000. In the year of purchase, capital allowances amount to £790,000 (the initial allowance of 75% and the first year writing down allowance of 4%). With Corporation Tax at 52%, the client will reduce his overall tax liability in the purchase year by £410,800, while the net present value of the total tax savings (assuming a net of inflation discount rate of 5%), will be approximately £485,000.

8.21 The impact on design choice of the capital allowances can also be significant. For example, in the case of a company involved in the storage, distribution and retailing of goods such as food, if the storage areas are located within the retailing units no capital allowances will be given. On the other hand, if the storage areas are combined as a distribution centre within a qualifying industrial unit, capital allowances are permitted.

Capital allowances for machinery, plant and equipment

8.22 As with buildings, so with machinery, plant and equipment. A distinction must be maintained between depreciation allowances for accounting purposes and capital allowances for taxation purposes. There need be no connection between the two.

8.23 Allowances are given for capital expenditure on machinery or plant used for the purpose of a trade, profession or employment. The expression 'machinery and plant' is widely interpreted for tax purposes. In the case of *Yarmouth v. France* (1887), 19, Q.B.D. 647 Lindley L.J. said that plant included 'whatever apparatus is used by a businessman for carrying on his business – not his stock-in-trade which he buys or makes for sale, but all goods and chattels, fixed or moveable, alive or dead, which he keeps for permanent employment in his business'.

* For discussion of some of these points, see V. E. Durkacz, *'Fine Tuning Industrial Building Allowances'*, in Building, 16 July 1982, p.17.

8.24 Another important case was *Jarrold v. John Good and Sons* [1963] AER 141 C.A. where it was held that demountable partitioning could not be rightly regarded as part of the premises, but could be regarded as plant. Two important concepts of the case were that plant can be construed as something which is not the subject of wear and tear, and plant can play a passive role in the operations of the trade.

8.25 Machinery and plant, therefore, includes machinery in the general sense and also such items as typewriters, desks, office equipment, carpets, curtains, demountable partitions, shop counters, and electrical fittings. Expenditure on repairs and maintenance or on renewal of parts, does not qualify for any of the capital allowances, but is considered to be a revenue trade expense and so is deductible.

8.26 Capital expenditure on alterations to an existing building, incidental to the installation of plant or machinery, may be treated as though it were expenditure on that machinery and so may qualify for the allowances. For example, if a new item of plant required a concrete machine base, drainage, and electrical connections, all the ancillary work including the excavation and concrete would qualify as plant because it would not have been necessary but for the new plant.

8.27 For these qualifying expenditures, the capital allowances take the following form.

- First year allowance.
- Writing down allowance.
- Pool of expenditure.
- Balancing charge.

8.28 The first year allowance for machinery and plant is 100% of the capital cost. The practical effect is that the full cost of plant is given whether the plant is new or second-hand. Companies are entitled to claim such part of the first year allowances as they consider advantageous. For example, if an item of plant is purchased for £5,000 the company may decide that in its particular circumstances, for instance, if it has a very low current tax liability, it will take only a £1,000 first year allowance. The balance of £4,000 is entitled to an annual writing down allowance of 25% in subsequent years.

8.29 In view of the nature of expenditure on items of plant and equipment and the complexity of calculation in a company's accounts, the writing down allowances do not usually have to be calculated separately for individual items of plant. The basis of the calculation is on the taxpayer's pool of expenditure. A company can disclaim any part of the writing down allowance. Thus, if the company makes a loss in the accounting period, it can, under current regulations, carry forward its allowances and set these against any future income from the trade.

8.30 For hire purchase agreements, the instalments payable are regarded as consisting of two parts. The first is the interest charge and the second the capital payment of part of the purchase price (cash price). The interest charge in each instalment is a revenue expense deductible in arriving at the trading income. The latter is a capital expenditure eligible for capital allowances.

8.31 It was noted above that current tax regulations with respect to buildings can significantly affect building design decisions. A similar situation arises with respect to machinery and plant.

8.32 It has already been indicated that demountable partitions qualify as plant. In buildings that do not qualify for capital allowances, such as offices, this could have an important effect on the choice of internal fittings.

8.33 Similarly, if a client constructing an office building has a choice between thermo-plastic tile flooring or carpeting, the vinyl tiles have no capital allowance whereas the carpet would have a 100% allowance by qualifying as plant and equipment. The after tax effect should be included in the life cycle cost comparison.

8.34 A further example is a computer installation where all the ancillary building work necessary to house the computer would be classed as being plant and equipment; for example the special air conditioning, electrical installation, special ducting and any additional structural work. The justification for this is that the fabric and ancillary equipment are essential for the computer equipment to function.

Regional development grants

8.35 Substantial grants and other financial help are available to encourage the establishment and growth of projects providing new employment in the areas for expansion in the U.K. Under Part 1 of the Industry Act 1972, regional development grants are available towards capital expenditure incurred in Special Development Areas and Development Areas in providing the following.

- New buildings or adaptations to existing buildings and premises used wholly or mainly for qualifying activities.

- New machinery or plant for use in premises used wholly or mainly for qualifying activities.

8.36 Qualifying activities referred to above are generally manufacturing industries, together with certain repair activities. The question whether any particular activity qualifies for a regional development grant is decided by the Department of Trade and Industry.

8.37 Regional development grants are not treated as reducing capital expenditure in computing tax allowances. Therefore in computing capital allowances, any grant is not deducted from the cost of the asset, nor does it affect the entitlement to first year or writing down allowance.

8.38 A detailed explanation of regional development grants is outside the scope of this book. Nevertheless, in qualifying areas and for qualifying buildings, the quantity surveyor must take account of the regional development grant in life cycle costing.

The role of the quantity surveyor in tax planning of buildings

8.39 There is a vital role for the quantity surveyor in providing advice to clients on the calculation of capital allowances for proposed buildings and building components. The profession needs to take a greater interest in the development of *taxation cost planning* as one of the professional services offered by surveyors. Clients make investment decisions on the basis of the best advice available to them at the time. More detailed information about the extent and the value of the capital allowances on projects will enhance their decision making capabilities. Advice could be given on assessment of capital allowances during the construction of a project, at the end of an accounting period, and at the completion of the project. Finally, help could be given in determining cash flows for feasibility studies.

8.40 Expenditure on plant equipment is eligible for capital allowances even if the building is not. The quantity surveyor should, therefore, consider the whole question of asset allocation. Expertise is necessary in the identification of those parts of the building that qualify as plant and equipment, and which are therefore eligible for the allowances.

8.41 In this respect, the bill of quantities has all the required information already itemized: all that is necessary is a logical restructuring of existing cost information. Each item in a bill of quantities should be examined to ascertain whether it is part of the building, or whether it could be considered as plant and equipment. This is perhaps most effectively analysed at the cost analysis stage using the BCIS elemental categories.

Items that qualify as machinery, plant and equipment

8.42 Table 8.A lists many of the items within a building that would normally qualify as machinery, plant and equipment for the purposes of capital allowances. The table is, of necessity, merely suggestive. Every project will have its own peculiarities and will require individual analysis in the manner suggested by the table.

8.43 All items within a building should be analysed into two categories.

- Building and external works.
- Plant and equipment.

The distinction between items which are part of the building and items which are plant and equipment is subject to negotiation with the Inland Revenue.

8.44 Generally, if an item of building work is required solely because of the plant and equipment, then the cost of the building work can be included within the plant and equipment category. An example of this is the cost of providing a plant room for the air-conditioning plant – the room being required solely to house and protect the equipment.

8.45 An appropriate adjustment should be made to all items to incorporate the value of preliminaries, and professional fees.

Table 8.A

Item	Plant and equipment
Finishes/fixtures/fittings	1. Wall finishes where they can be removed from the building, *e.g.* curtains, curtain track, battens for fixing 2. Floor finishes such as carpets and any floor finishing that can be removed from the building 3. Door mats and matwell frames 4. Suspended ceilings which are airtight and can be used as an extract system or any ceiling which is an integral part of the heating, ventilating or air-conditioning system 5. Any movable fixtures and fittings 6. Demountable partitions 7. Curtains, blinds and furnishing 8. Cupboards, lockers, shelves, display counters, chalkboards, dustbins, cloakroom fittings, telephone booths
Plumbing and sanitary services	1. Sanitary fittings (not the pipework) 2. Vanitory units 3. Soap dispensers 4. Mirrors 5. Demountable toilet partitions 6. Coat hooks and racks 7. Towel rails and cabinets 8. Toilet roll holders 9. Tanks
Heat source	1. Boilers and equipment, fuel pumps, water pumps, flue, etc. (not the pipework from the boiler) 2. Boiler bases and foundations 3. Oil storage tanks and foundations 4. Fuel hoppers, ash removal plant 5. Control equipment to the heating system 6. Builder's work in connection with the heat source 7. Part cost of boiler room
Space heating and air treatment	1. Equipment in connection with heating, air-conditioning and hot water installation (not the pipework or ducting) 2. Builder's work in connection with the equipment 3. Plant room 4. Electrical and mechanical control systems 5. Solar heating systems 6. Insulation to pipework 7. Independent heaters
Ventilating systems	1. Dust and fume extraction equipment including ductwork and builders' work in connection 2. Extract fans and builder's work 3. Ventilators 4. Instrumentation controls

Item	Plant and equipment
Electrical installations	1. Electrical installation to all plant and equipment (excludes conduit and wiring to power and lighting for the building generally) 2. Light fittings 3. Emergency lighting 4. Switchgear and transformers 5. Control gear and distribution boards 6. Plant rooms 7. Builder's work in connection with the electrical installation
Gas installations	1. Gas fires, cookers and equipment including flues and builder's work in connection
Lift and conveyor installations	1. Lift installation complete including builder's work in connection and lift motors, lift guides and plant room 2. Escalators and hoists are as for lifts
Communication installations	1. Clocks 2. Sound distribution, bells, signals and the like 3. Fire alarms 4. Burglar alarms 5. Telephone installation 6. Builder's work in connection with communication installations
Special installations/protective installations	1. Sprinkler system 2. Dry riser system 3. Hosereel system 4. CO_2 system 5. Fire extinguishers 6. Refrigeration equipment 7. Kitchen equipment 8. Laundry equipment 9. Health equipment 10. Laboratory equipment 11. Manufacturing equipment 12. Incinerators and flues 13. Water heaters 14. Hand dryers 15. Window cleaning hoists and equipment including track, motors and ancillary builder's work 16. Refuse disposal equipment including ancillary builder's work 17. Lightning conductors and earthing systems 18. Occupational equipment associated with the building user 19. Computer equipment and all ancillary work 20. Crane gantries 21. All builder's work in connection with items 1. to 20. above
Special items within a building (the items shown are only given as indicative of the types of item)	1. Removable fire escapes 2. Shelving 3. Safes and strong rooms 4. Roller shutters 5. Ladders 6. Dock levellers 7. Signs/notice boards 8. Interior planting
External works	1. External signs 2. Traffic signs, crash barriers 3. Drainage where it is specifically required for plant and equipment 4. Cycle racks

9

A worked example

Introduction

9.1   The worked example detailed below gives the life cycle cost plan for a particular design option for a 240 place primary school. No attempt has been made to compare these costs with the costs of other design options, the intention being to illustrate in some detail the application of the techniques discussed in previous chapters.

9.2   If alternative designs are to be compared, similar calculations should be performed for each option. In doing so there will, of course, be many areas in which cost estimates are common to the various possibilities, thus saving computational effort.

9.3   The example has been provided by Essex County Council using a base date of November 1982. A discount rate of 2% has been used which takes due account of inflation. This reflects the view of the County Council with respect to the difference between the cost of capital to the Council and forecast inflation rates (recall the discussion in chapter 4).

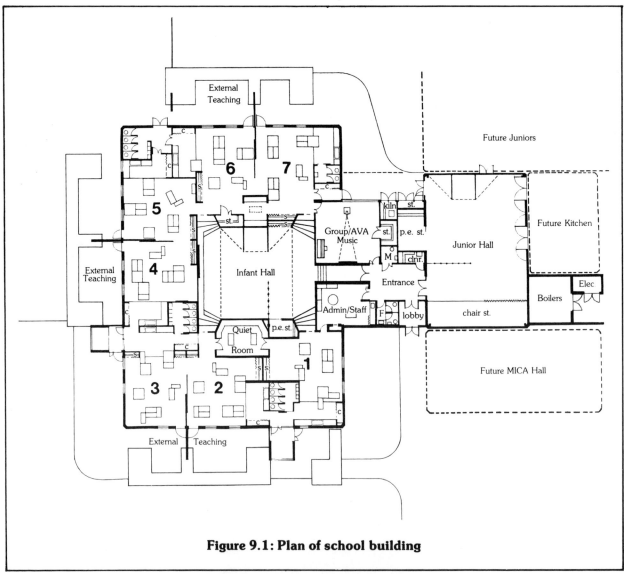

Figure 9.1: Plan of school building

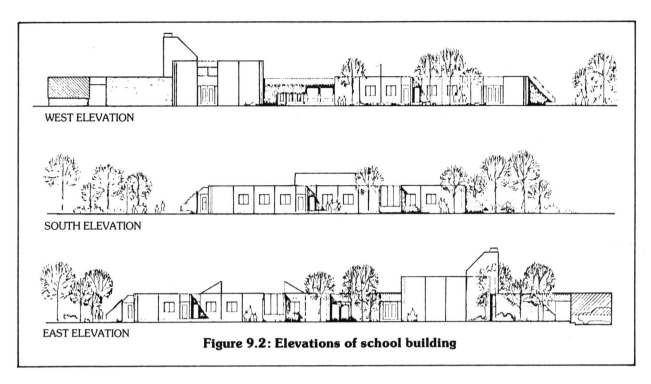

WEST ELEVATION

SOUTH ELEVATION

EAST ELEVATION

Figure 9.2: Elevations of school building

9.4 The life cycle for the analysis is 30 years. Note that this is an estimate of the functional life of the building, not the physical life (recall the discussion in chapter 2).

9.5 The estimated fuel use has been calculated in accordance with the model set out in the Department of Education and Science Design Note 17.

9.6 *Figure 9.1* and *figure 9.2* show the plan and elevations of the school building used for the worked example.

Life cycle cost plan

General information
Project   : 240 place primary school
Location   : Essex
Date   : November 1982
Discount rate : 2% (net)
Life cycle   : 30 years

Description of proposed building
Steel and concrete framed single storey building, flat roof, low pressure hot water heating system. Associated external works.

Sources of data
1. Cleaning and caretaking – County formula
2. Grounds maintenance   – County schedule of works values
3. County and district rates – Essex Local Government Finance 1982/3
4. Sewerage charges   – Anglian Water Authority
5. Water charges   – Essex Water Company
6. Insurances   – County Insurance Officer
7. Energy   – CIBS Guide. DES Design Note 17. Current Gas and Electricity Board Tariff
8. Maintenance   – Chief building surveyor's maintenance records

Assumptions

Occupancy   – 8½ hours per day, 5 days per week excluding holidays. No evening use.

Life cycle   – Use of building assumed indefinite but life cycle restricted to 30 years. No disposal costs or residual value included. Assumes current restriction on internal redecoration will be relaxed in the near future.

Discount rate – Assumed that the major cost elements, *viz* energy and labour, will inflate at approximately the same rate. Therefore single discount factor used.

Measurement

Building data

Gross floor area	904 m²
Circulation space area	80 m²
Ground floor area	904 m²
Volume	2,440 m³
Upper floor area	– m²
Roof area	904 m²
Wall area (net)	316 m²
Windows and external door area (net)	106 m²
Internal walls and partitions area	420 m²
Internal doors area	70 m²
Wall finishes area	840 m²
Floor finishes area	830 m²
Ceiling finishes area	813 m²
Fittings and furnishings	– nr
Sanitary appliances	56 nr
Water installation (draw off points)	93 nr
Site works	10,000 m²

Design data

No. of occupants	243 nr
Occupants/m² gross floor area	0.27
Net/gross floor area	84%

Brief specification: Concrete light aggregate wall panels, aluminium windows, Durox and asphalt flat roof, fairface blockwork partitions with sigmulta, generally carpet floor covering, low pressure hot water heating system with steel radiators, fluorescent lighting.

Life cycle cost plan – worksheet

1. Capital cost

From Essex County Council Building Economics Unit Model for 240 place primary.

Building 904m² @ £316.37 =	£286,000
External works (from model)	£ 52,000
	£338,000 (October 1982 firm price)
Design charges etc	£ 60,000
	£398,000

2. Operation costs (annual)

	Cost per annum £

2.1 Caretaking

Gfa 904 plus 28m² covered court = 932m²
From County Schedule, 1 caretaker required — 5,200

2.2 Cleaning

a) Floor and general cleaning

From County Schedule total hours 39 per week
Less caretaker contribution 20

Part-time cleaner 19 hours per week

Cleaner 19 hours @ £2.00 × 52 weeks = £1,976
Materials = £ 250
Equipment replacement and
maintenance say = £ 200 — 2,426

b) Window cleaning

Twice annually @ £27 = £54 — 54

Total cleaning = £7,680

(£8.50/m²)

Present value (30 years) = £172,000

(£190.27/m²)

114

2.3 Rates

From National Rating Formula for Schools

Teaching area plus teaching storage	= 622m²
Less 10% for open plan	= 62m²

560m² ÷ 1.9 = 295 scholar places

Rating calculation:

Gross value

1. Basic price £16.25 plus £1.10 for high site value

	= £17.35 × 295	=	5,118
2. Kitchen	5.3m² × 42m²	=	223
3. Caretaker		=	
4. Playing fields	£150/ha × 1ha	=	150
			5,491

$$\text{Rateable Value} = \frac{10\,(5{,}491 - 34)}{12} = 4{,}548$$

District rate : 4,548 @ 11.30p in £	=	514
County rate : 4,548 @ 125.90p in £	=	5,726
Sewerage charge : 4,548 @ 18.65p in £	=	848
Water charges : 160,000 galls. @ 84p/1000 galls.	=	134
Standing water charge	=	29

Total rates & water charges = £7,251
(£8.02/m²)

Present value (30 years) = £162,400
(£179.65/m²)

2.4 Insurances
(Part fire insurance only)

Building cost : £286,000
Premium rate: 80p/£1000

Annual premium = £230
(0.25/m²)
Present value (30 years) = £5,150
(5.70/m²)

2.5 Staff

Administrative staff (establishment related only) = £7,500 p.a.   (£8.30/m²)
Present value (30 years) = £168,000
(£185.84/m²)

2.6 Energy

(Calculation follows the principles of DES Design Note 17)

Heat losses

a) **Fabric**

Element	Area		U Value		W/°C	Temp. diff.	Conv. to kW	kW
Ground Floor	904m²	×	0.3	=	271.2			
Roof	904m²	×	0.5	=	452.0			
Opaque Wall	316m²	×	1.3	=	410.8			
Windows	106m²	×	5.6	=	593.6			
					1,727.6 ×	19° ÷	1000	= 32.82

b) **Ventilation   Occupants   Air change/person**

243   ×   30m³   × 0.33 × 19° ÷   1000 = 45.70
Total loss = 78.52kW

c) **Less gains**

			kW
Occupants	: 243 × 70W/person	÷ 1000	= 17.01
Lighting	: 12W/m² (DES) × 904	÷ 1000	= 10.85
Miscellaneous power	: 3W/m² × 904	÷ 1000	= 2.71 **Less** 30.57

Net heat loss = 47.95kW

Annual energy cost

Natural gas	Total loss (kW)		Running hours		Calorific value		Price/ therm		Cost
1. Heating	47.95	×	1731	÷	29.3	×	50.7p	=	1,436
2. Hot water (kitchen)	12500			÷	29.3	×	50.7p	=	216
							Gas total =		£1,652

Electricity

1. Lighting $\dfrac{52}{3.73}$ (kW/m²/a) × 904m² × 5.5p = 693

	W/m²	Hours/per annum	
2. Local hot water	2.00 ×	400	= 800
3. Power	3.00 ×	1,400	= 4,200
4. Pumps	2.00 ×	1,120	= 2,240

7,240 × 904m² ÷ 1000 × 5.5p

= 360

Electricity total = £1,053

Energy total cost per annum = £ 2,705
(£2.99/m²)

Present value = £60,500
(£60.92/m²)

3. Maintenance costs

3.1 Annual

a) Building

	Cost/per annum £
1. Heating and hot water services plant (term contract)	300
2. Replacement of fluorescent tubes and bulbs 904m² @ 6p	= 54
3. Minor repairs 904m² @ 50p	= 452

Building total = £806
(0.89m²)

b) External works

		£
Grounds maintenance for 1ha site	Labour	700
	Fuel and maintenance	150

External works = 850

Total annual maintenance = £1,656

Present value (30 years) = £37,100

3.2 Intermittent

Item	Quantity	Maintenance/ replacement cost (unit rate)	Interval (years)	Proportion replaced	Cost £	PVF	PV £
Roof covering Asphalt	936m²	£25/m²	30	100%	23400	0.5521	12920
External walls Panel joints	186m	£3.15/m	15	100%	586	1.2951	760
Windows & doors Anodised aluminium windows	92m²	£100	30	15%	1380	0.5521	760
Softwood doors	14m²	£160 (Rep.)	20	15%	1120	0.6730	750
	14m²	£3 (Redec.)	6	100%	42	3.5505	150
Internal walls Sigmulta wall finishes	2074m²	£3.75/m²	15	100%	7778	1.2951	10080
Floor finishes Carpet (classrooms)	400m²	£4.75/m²	15	75%	1900	1.2951	2460
Carpet (circulation)	71m²	£4.75/m²	10	100%	337	2.0454	690
Carpet (admin)	48m²	£4.75/m²	20	50%	95	0.6730	60
Granwood	125m²	£3.00/m² (sanding)	10	100%	375	2.0454	770
Vinyl	186m²	£10.67/m²	30	75%	1488	0.5521	820
Ceilings Emulsion paint	813m²	£1.78/m²	10	90%	1300	2.0456	2660
Heating 70kW gas boiler	1 Nr	£2750	30	100%	2750	0.5521	1520
Control equipment	1 Nr	£1500	20	50%	750	0.6730	500
Pumps	2 Nr	£300	30	100%	600	0.5521	330
Hot water Calorifier	1 Nr	£750	30	100%	750	0.5521	410
Pumps	2 Nr	£100	30	100%	200	0.5521	110
Local water heaters	6 Nr	£50	20	50%	150	0.6730	100
Lighting & power Allow contingency	–	£1500	15	100%	1500	1.2951	1940
					Building present value = 37790		
					Present value/m² = £41.80/m²		
External works Playgrounds & road surfaces	2220m²	£350	20	90%	6993	0.6730	4700
Fences & gates	–	£500	30	100%	500	0.5521	270
					External works present value		£4970

```
Building present value          =   £37790
External works present value    =    £4970
                                     ──────
                                     £42760
Building and engineering surveyors charges  =   £5140
                                     ──────
                                     £47900
```

Intermittent maintenance total present value say £48000

Life cycle cost plan summary

Project: 240 place primary school
Location: Essex
Date: November 1982

Costs	Estimated target costs	Present value
1. Capital costs		
Building	336,750	336,750
External works	61,250	61,250
Total capital costs	398,000	398,000
2. Running costs		
2.1 Operation costs		
Energy	2,705	60,500
Caretaking and cleaning	7,680	172,000
Rates	7,251	162,400
Insurances	230	5,150
Staff	7,500	168,000
Total operations costs	25,366	568,050
2.2 Maintenance costs (annual)		
Building	806	18,050
External works	850	19,050
Total maintenance costs (annual)	1,656	37,100
2.3 Maintenance/replacement/ alteration costs (intermittent)		
Building	–	42,300
External works	–	5,700
Total maintenance/replacement/ alteration costs (intermittent)	–	48,000
2.4 Sundries	250	5,600
Total sundries	250	5,600
Total running costs	–	658,750
3. Additional tax allowances		NIL
4. Salvage and residuals		NIL
5. Occupancy costs (Excluded)		–
Total occupancy costs		–

Total present value of life cycle costs =   £1,056,750

Annual equivalent value of life cycle costs =   £ 47,200

Full year effect costs
Note: All costs at November 1982 prices.

1. **Capital repayment**	**Building**	**(£/m²)**	**Extl. works**	**Total**
£398,000 debt charges:	47,200	(52.21)	8,600	55,800
2. **Annual costs (from LCCP summary)**				
2.1 Operations costs	25,366	(28.06)	–	25,366
2.2 Annual maintenance	806	(0.89)	850	1,656
2.3 Sundries	250	(0.28)	–	250
2. **Intermittent costs (from LCCP summary)**				
Present value : £48,000				
Annual equivalent : £48,000 ÷ 22.3965*	1,890	(2.09)	253	2,143
*(YP for 30 years 2%)				
	£75,512	(83.53)	£9,703	£85,215

Full year effect costs		
(year 1 at current prices)		**£85,215**

10

Summary and conclusions

10.1 A life cycle cost approach is essential to decision-making in the building industry for the very simple reason that buildings are durable assets. In looking at the cost of a building it is far too short-sighted to consider merely the initial acquisition costs. Attention must also be paid to the subsequent running costs associated with the operation and maintenance of the building fabric and individual building components.

10.2 It can no longer be argued that because initial capital costs are the most important costs of purchasing and operating a building, good decision-making need only consider capital costs. The analysis within previous chapters of this book has shown that a trade-off exists between capital costs and running costs. There are, therefore, important cost savings to be made by shaking loose from the traditional concern purely with capital costs.

10.3 A life cycle cost approach is not applicable solely to the efficient design of complete new buildings. The approach offers important cost savings when applied to decisions with respect to the existing building stock and when applied to the choice of individual building components. To put it simply, any area of building design, operation or maintenance that has associated costs over time should benefit from a life cycle cost approach.

10.4 As a decision-making tool then, a life cycle cost approach offers significant benefits to clients of the building industry, but this is not its only use. Life cycle cost should also be seen as a management tool. It can be used to identify short term running costs of buildings or building components for cash flow purposes. It should also be used to monitor running costs of such buildings or building components, since by doing so it will be possible to identify areas in which cost savings might be achieved either by a change in operating conditions or by changing the building component.

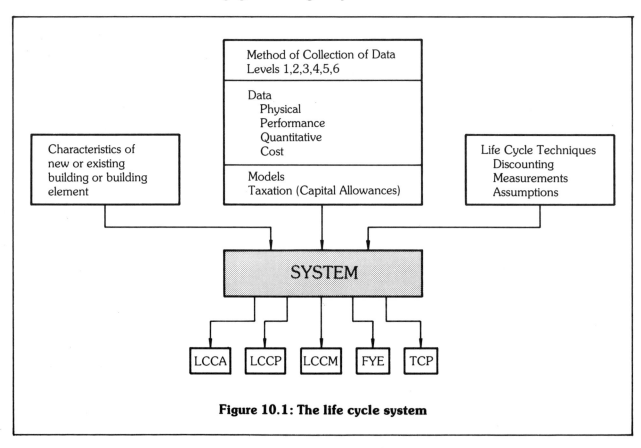

Figure 10.1: The life cycle system

10.5 The various uses of life cycle cost and the basic methodology of the approach are summarised in *figure 10.1*. These comprise four main components – data, a series of techniques, a system for applying techniques to data, and output. The output takes a number of forms depending upon the objectives – life cycle cost analysis, planning or management, full year effect costs, or a taxation cost plan.

10.6 It should be emphasised that life cycle costing as a concept is not new. It uses tried and tested economic principles long applied to investment appraisal in many spheres of industrial and commercial activity.

10.7 A number of good reasons can be advanced as to why professional consultants in the building industry have been slow to implement life cycle costing.

- The diverse nature of the industry's clients, with very different client motivations.

- The complex and theoretical relationship between money now and money spent or received in the future.

- Relatively cheap energy supplies.

- Frequently changing rate of inflation.

- The long time lag between the design process and data becoming available on the running costs of proposed buildings or building systems.

- A lack of reliable and adequate data on running costs structured in a useful format.

- Difficulty in forecasting future events in the life of a building and its components.

- The sensitivity of future estimates of running costs for private sector buildings to changes in taxation legislation.

- The natural concentration by building consultants on services for which they are paid and, therefore, those in demand.

10.8 In particular there has been a lack of a coherent system whereby the ideas inherent in the approach can be applied in a consistent manner. This book has addressed the issues stated above and supplies a system with the following attributes.

- It focusses attention upon the relationship between the capital cost and the running costs of buildings and building components.

- It provides a methodology and framework to enable the design team to estimate the total cost of what could happen, what should happen and what will happen.

- It provides a check list of occupancy cost items to encourage the design team to bridge the gap between the design and construction phase and the occupancy phase of a building's life.

- It uses information contained in bills of quantities and on drawings as a basis for a life cycle cost management system for new or existing buildings. This will identify those areas in which the running costs might be reduced, either by a change in operating practice or by replacing the relevant system. It is also important to the design team that there is a feed-back on the cost and performance of the building in use.

- It structures the data in a hierarchy of levels, thus allowing a more co-ordinated approach to capturing cost information and performance data for both new and existing buildings.

- It evaluates the total costs of design options in a simple manner.

10.9 No mention has been made of the question of an appropriate scale of professional charges for providing life cycle cost advice, nor has the question of professional liability been discussed. It is not envisaged that a nationally recommended scale of charges would be prepared for life cycle costing in view of the complicated and diverse nature of the task. Experience in the United States of America and Canada implies that fees based upon hourly or daily charge for professional services could be adopted, but a lump sum fee is also an option.

10.10 It is beyond the scope of this book to discuss the legal and insurance problems of professional liability for life cycle cost advice. This issue is, however, important and will require detailed consideration.

10.11 It should be emphasised, once again, that while the results of the analysis may look very precise and convincing, there is no substitute for professional skill and judgement when applying life cycle cost techniques. The techniques are purely a tool for decision-making.

10.12 Selling professional services in the competitive market place is difficult, particularly in view of the traditional conservatism of the building industry. It is to be hoped, however, that consultant quantity surveyors will now be better able to convince both public and private sector clients of the undoubted advantages and benefits to be gained from a life cycle cost approach to the purchase and use of their buildings. This can only benefit the entire construction industry.

Bibliography

Blacker J.
Maintenance Manual and Job Diary.
The Building Centre, 1980.

Blanchard B. F.
Design and Manage to Life Cycle Cost.
M/A Press, Portland, Oregon, 1978.

Bottle P. F.
The Economics of Adaptability: A comparative study of the initial and life costs of partitions – Paper No. 4.
Laboratories Investigation Unit, Department of Education and Science, 1971.

Bowen B. & Charette R.
Energy Economics and Life Cycle Costing.
Royal Architectural Institute of Canada, 1980.

British Institute of Cleaning Science
Cleaning Industry Handbook.
British Institute of Cleaning Science, 1982.

Bromwich M.
The Economics of Capital Budgeting.
Penguin, 1977.

Brown R. S. et al.
Economic Analysis Handbook, U.S. Naval Facilities Engineering Command, Alexandria, VA, June 1975.

Building Maintenance Cost Information Service
Building Maintenance Price Book.
B.M.C.I.S. 1980.

Building Owners and Management Association International
1979 Downtown and Suburban Office Building Experience Exchange Report. B.O.M.A. Washington D.C. 1979.

Buckman D., Reynold J. & Gapper J.
Decision-making in Building Maintenance.
Local Government Operational Research Unit, 1970.

Burberry P.
Predictions of Thermal Performance, 1, 2 and 3. Architects Journal 24/31 October, 7 November 1979, pp 893-905, 951, 962, 993-1062.

Centre for Advanced Land Use Studies
Land Use Control Handbook.
College of Estate Management, 1981.

Chartered Institution of Building Services
CIBS Guide: Volume A, Design Data.
The Chartered Institution of Building Services, 1981.

Chartered Institution of Building Services
CIBS Guide B18: Owning and Operating Costs.
The Chartered Institution of Building Services, 1977.

Chartered Institution of Building Services
Building Energy Code: Part 2 Calculation of energy demands and targets for the design of new buildings and services.
The Chartered Institution of Building Services, 1981.

Clifton R. H.
Principles of Planned Maintenance.
Edward Arnold (Publishers) Ltd. 1974.

Committee for Industrial Technologies
The Total Cost of Ownership – Tero-technology Concept and Practice.
Department of Industry, H.M.S.O. 1975.

Committee for Terotechnology   *Maintenance Aspects of Terotechnology –*
Planned Maintenance.
Department of Industry, 1975.

Committee for Terotechnology   *Design Aspects of Terotechnology – Policy and*
Practice.
Department of Industry, 1975.

Committee for Terotechnology   *Management Aspects of Terotechnology – Life*
Cycle Costing.
Department of Industry, 1975.

Committee for Terotechnology   *Terotechnology in Small Firms – Guidelines for*
Owner/Managers.
Department of Industry, 1976.

Committee for Terotechnology   *Building Aspects of Terotechnology – The*
Management of Physical Resources: Building
and Services.
Department of Industry, 1977.

Committee for Terotechnology   *Terotechnology Handbook.*
Department of Industry, H.M.S.O. 1978.

Day P. H.   *Capital Investment Appraisal for Mechanical*
and Electrical Services in Commercial
Buildings.
Heating and Ventilating Engineer, February
1976, 50, (583) pp 4-7.

Debenham Tewson &   *Office Rent and Rates 1973-1982.*
Chinnocks   Debenham Tewson & Chinnocks, London.
April 1982.

Department of Education &   *Energy Conservation in Educational Buildings*,
Science   H.M.S.O. 1977.

Department of Education &   *Energy Conservation in Two Oxfordshire*
Science   *Schools – Design Note 16.*
Department of Education and Science,
Architects and Building, Branch, 1978.

Department of Education &   *Guidelines for Environmental Design and Fuel*
Science   *Conservation in Educational Buildings –*
Design Note 17.
Department of Education and Science,
Architects and Buildings Branch, 1981.

Department of Industry   *Life Cycle Costing in the Management of*
Assets: A Practical Guide.
H.M.S.O. 1977

Durkacz V. E.   *Fine Tuning Industrial Building Allowances.*
Building, 16 July 1982, p.17.

Ebenfelt H.   *Some Experience from the Use of an LCC*
Approach. Annals of Assurance Sciences
Symposium on Reliability and Maintainability,
Los Angeles, 29-31 January 1974, pp
142-146.

Economic Commission for   *Cost, Repetition, Maintenance – Related*
Europe   *Aspects of Building Prices*, (Ch. 3. *Durability*
and Lifetime),
United Nations, 1963.

Elliott D. A.   *Costs in Use: Some Words of Caution.*
Building Technology and Management, May
1978, pp 3-6.

Forster R. & Matthews D. B.

How to Get Value from your Lighting Installation. Electrical Times, 30 November 1979, 4549, 9, p. 12.

General Accounting Office

Increased Competition can Reduce Elevator Maintenance and Cleaning Service Costs. General Accounting Office. Washington D.C. Report no. PSAD-78-115, 1978.

General Electric Co.

Energy Use in Office Buildings: Volume 1 – Analysis of 1977 Office Building Energy Use. General Electric Co. 1980.

Haviland D. S.

Life Cycle Cost Analysis – Using it in Practice. American Institute of Architects, 1978.

Haviland D. S.

Life Cycle Cost Analysis – A Guide for Architects. American Institute of Architects, 1977.

Haworth D. P.

Life Cycle Costing – Paper from Conference Proceedings "Long Term Economy – the Real Cost of Buildings". Harvard Graduate School, November 3-4, 1975.

Hewgill J. C. R.

Towards Economic Life Cycle Costs,, Ch.2 Terotechnology Handbook, pp 12-20. Department of Industry, 1978.

H.M.S.O.

General Rate Act, 1967. H.M.S.O. 1976 (Reprinted)

Holmes R., Droop, C. & Mellor P.

Coding Systems for House Maintenance, Housing Research Unit, Department of Surveying, Bristol Polytechnic, November 1982.

Howell R. G. & Renold J.

Data on the Deterioration of Building Elements. Local Government Operational Research Unit, 1970.

Kirk S. J. & Dell'Isola A. J.

Life Cycle Costing for Design Professionals. McGraw Hill, 1981.

Lansdowne D. K.

Life Cycle – A Study. David K. Lansdowne & Partners Ltd. Ontario, Canada, 1976.

Levy H. & Sarnat M.

Capital Investment and Financial Decisions. Prentice Hall International (2nd edition).

Lewis J. D.

Planning Painting for Minimum Costs-in-Use. Department of the Environment, Construction, 21.

Lokmanhekim M.

Energy Utilisation Analysis of Building. University of California, Department of Energy, 1978.

Lovely J. D.

Durability, Reliability and Serviceability. ASHRAE Journal (USA), January 1973, 15, (1). pp 67-69.

Lush D.

Better Energy Audits. Building Services, November 1982, pp 45-50.

125

Marshall H. E. & Ruegg R. T.   *Energy Conservation in Buildings: An Economics Guidebook for Investment Decisions*. National Bureau of Standards, Washington D.C. May 1980.

Marshall H. E. & Ruegg R. T.   *Energy Conservation through Life Cycle Costing*. Journal of Architectural Education. Vol. 30. February 1977, pp 42-53.

Marshall H. E. & Ruegg R. T.   *Simplified Energy Design Economics*. Centre for Building Technology, National Bureau of Standards, Washington D.C. 1978.

National Economic Development Office   *Construction for Industrial Recovery*. National Economic Development Office, H.M.S.O. 1978.

Peat, Marwick, Mitchell & Co.   *Finance for New Projects in the United Kingdom – A Guide to Government Incentives*. Peat, Marwick, Mitchell & Co. London, 1982.

Pickerill R. J.   *Capital Allowances in Law and Practice*. The Institute of Chartered Accountants in England and Wales, 1981.

Purkis H. J., How R. F. C., Hooper N. J. & Poole M. T.   *Occupancy Costs of Offices*. Building Research Establishment, CP 44/77, August 1977.

Rakhra A. S.   *Building and Life Cycle Costing*. National Research Council of Canada, Canadian Building Digest, July 1980, pp 212-1/214-4;

Reynolds, Smith & Hills   *Life Cycle Costing Emphasising Energy Conservation Guidelines for Investment Analysis*. Reynolds, Smith & Hills, Architects, Jacksonville, Florida, May 1977.

Robson Rhodes   *A Review of Capital Allowances Available to Persons Trading in the U.K.* Robson Rhodes, Chartered Accountants, London April 1983.

Roose R. W.   *Handbook of Energy Conservation for Mechanical Systems in Buildings*. Van Nostrand Reinhold, 1978.

Royal Institution of Chartered Surveyors   *Building Management Manuals: A Guide for Practitioners*. Surveyors Publications, 1981.

Royal Institution of Chartered Surveyors   *Planned Building Maintenance*: Practice Note No. 4. Surveyors Publications, 1980

Royal Institution of Chartered Surveyors   *Property Insurance*. Surveyors Publications, 1978.

Ruegg R. et. al.   *Life Cycle Costing, A Guide for Selecting Energy Projects for Public Buildings*. National Bureau of Standards, Washington D.C. Building Science Series, No. 113, 1978.

Ruegg R. T. & Chapman R.E.   *Economic Evaluation of Windows in Buildings: Methodology*. U.S. Department of Commerce: National Bureau of Standards, Washington D.C., 1979.

Ruegg R. T.	*Life Cycle Cost Manual for the Federal Energy Management Programme.* National Bureau of Standards, Washington D.C. December 1980.
Ruegg R. T., Petersen S. R. & Marshall, H. E.	*Recommended Practice for Measuring Life Cycle Costs of Buildings and Building Systems.* U.S. Department of Commerce, 1980.
Russell A. D.	*Economic Risks in Energy Conservation Strategies.* (Unpublished paper). Concordia University, Montreal, Canada, 1980.
Russell A. D.	*Economic Evaluation of Building Energy Systems.* Proceedings First Canadian Building Congress: Energy and Buildings, Toronto 25th to 27th October 1976.
Stevens A. J.	*The Economics of Buildings: Life Cycle Costing.* M.Sc. Thesis submitted to Faculty of Fine Art and Architecture at University of Cape Town, October 1978.
Stone P. A.	*Building Economy.* Pergamon Press, 3rd edition, 1983.
Stone P. A.	*Building Design Evaluation: Costs in Use.* E. & F.N. Spon, 1980.
Tucker S. N.	*Assessment of Office Building Proposals.* The Valuer, Australia, 24 (1), January 1976, pp 16-25.
Tucker S. N.	*Economic Assessment Criteria for Building Investment.* The Building Economist, Australia, 17 (4) March 1979, pp 155-162.
U.S. Department of Energy	*Energy Audit Workbook for Warehouses.* U.S. Department of Energy, Washington D.C. September 1978 (DoE CS 0041-9).
Welch L.	*Out of Town Office Space.* Chartered Surveyor Weekly, February 10 1983, pp 316-317.
White E. N.	*Maintenance Planning, Control and Documentation.* Gower Press, 1979.
Zimmerman L. W. & Hart G. D.	*Value Engineering: A Practical Approach for Owners, Designers and Contractors.* Van Nostrand Reinhold 1982 Ch.8 pp 150-172.